The soul is highest, noblest,
worthiest when it is lowest,
humblest, and gentlest.

~ Julian of Norwich

For Graham and Delta

THE
NAKED
TRUTH
ABOUT
BREAST
CANCER

JANE MARSHALL

Contents

About Jane

Born in Glasgow in 1969, I'm very much a product of my generation: a Gen X woman brought up by my mum to aim high.

I spent my teens as a political activist, and at 17 I got myself onto the National Executive Committee of the National Union of Students. I spent 2 years standing on tabletops in student bars or marching at the front of demonstrations with a megaphone.

I spent the next decade working in small start-ups during the first dot com boom. I set up some of the UK's first digital companies when no-one had even heard of the internet and the web browser hadn't been invented yet. I became a Director in one of Europe's largest media companies, responsible for a bunch of world-firsts. I was a leader in my field - I featured regularly in the national media and on conference platforms.

I took a 2 year career break at 40 and travelled the world solo, going wherever the wind took me. I skied in Switzerland, visited Cambodia, lived in Mexico City for 6 months learning Spanish. I went to the Pacific and learnt to dive - going on to spend a year living on the tiny island of Palau, a long way from anywhere working on a dive boat.

In 2010 I came to Australia and spent 8 years in senior roles in a large global telco. I went on to run my own strategy and innovation business.

I had a strong spiritual practise and meditated every day. I looked after my body, ate well, slept well, didn't smoke or drink much, and was fit and strong. I took up powerlifting in my forties and am the proud holder of a handful of Australian records. I was training for world records.

I was brave, a go-anywhere do-anything kind of woman. I've had the great fortune to live an interesting life. I've been incredibly lucky in my career. There was nothing I wouldn't - or couldn't - do. And I wasn't finished. I had plans: a long list of places to visit, and things to do. I was only 50.

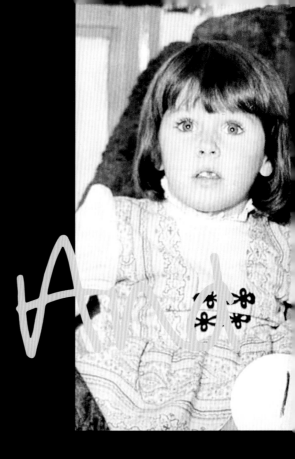

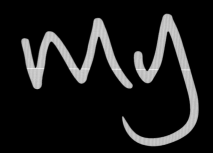

Here I Am

2 years in. Doing my best to get back to some kind of life.

But here's the truth. I feel unwell most of the time. I'm still exhausted, often dizzy, discombobulated. My body's a mess. The menopause is awful. The meds to stop the cancer coming back are unbearable. Facing death has been a huge shock. There is the worry of the cancer coming back.

I've lost friends, and several people I loved dearly. I can't go back to the kind of work I used to do. I don't know who I am any more. My old life is gone and there is no way back. I don't know what happens next.

This has been devastating. It's as if a bomb went off in my life and there is nothing left.

And yet... A lot of wonderful and extraordinary things have happened too. I know more about love and life than I ever have, and I'm almost able to say I wouldn't change any of it. It has been a most profound journey into the mystic.

It's changed everything.

I Am Here.

C-View

everything

About the book

This is a book from my heart to yours. It's a labour of love.

From the moment I heard the words 'you have breast cancer' I documented everything – I took photos, kept a journal, kept all my medical notes. I published some blogs, but most of what I wrote I kept private. I write because it helps me make sense of things and what was happening to me was surreal. It wasn't just breast cancer.

It was living alone in the world's longest lockdown, coming home from chemo to an empty house, going without any form of human touch during the hardest time of my life. It was watching the pandemic overseas and noting that people with cancer were vulnerable and dying. It was watching the news of the first covid deaths in Melbourne – cancer patients in a cancer ward – and wondering if covid was going to kill me if the cancer didn't. It was extreme menopause and all that this brings.

When it came to cancer, I had absolutely no idea what I was doing. I've never seen any kind of cancer up close, and I had to work it out as I went along. It was only later I realised that what I wrote might be useful to other women who hear those same words and who have no idea what they're doing either. This is the book you need when you get your diagnosis: It's all the things that no-one ever talks about, and that your surgeon, doctor, oncologist either can't or don't tell you. Knowing what's happening is incredibly empowering.

It's not an ordinary book. It's raw, unedited, and unfiltered. Nothing is off limits. There's nudity, swearing, and the full depths of my own misery and suffering, even though at times it's excruciating to see it on the page.

Because that is the naked truth about breast cancer.

Our cancer is seen as a 'good' cancer, which means that survival rates are high relative to others. But that only tells half the story – breast cancer is absolutely brutal, arduous, and very lonely. I want to show the reality of the thing: the emotional and spiritual rollercoaster, the devastation. For many of us, nothing is ever the same again.

Much of this goes unspoken. There are a number of reasons for this I think. In part it's because there's still so much shame around women's bodies and breasts – and by extension breast cancer. Then there's the trauma. It's as if it's too traumatic to speak of, and most others don't understand it, so we pack it away somewhere and just get on. There's the idea that we should just be grateful to be alive and not complain, no matter how scarred we are by what we've had to do to survive. And then there's death. Talking about our own mortality is one of the last taboos in our society. We're asked to focus on survival rates, to pretend that the spectre of death isn't there, and stay positive!

It is specifically NOT a how-to-do-breast-cancer book – it's just the story of how I did it. There is no one way to do it. And there is no 'good' way to do it either. Breast cancer is hard, it's hard for all of us. However hard you're finding it, I want you to know you're not failing. Just getting up every day, putting one foot in front of the other, and doing your best is a victory.

The heart of the book is really about extreme adversity. Yes, cancer is shit and at the same time something extraordinary happens in the depths of our grief. This is not a Pollyanna book; it's not an attempt to pretend the horrors of this thing are anything other than what they are, to paper over the destruction this thing wreaks in our lives. But at the same time there is consolation for us. In the face of such great adversity everything and everyone else falls away, and it's just You and Life. We have no option then, but to face inwards – to dig deep. And when we do, often when we're at our lowest point, we find what the great mystics wrote about – the light of our own soul.

It's therefore a momentous rite of passage: one of those moments when we walk through a door and there is no going back, we're changed forever. I call this The Heroine's Journey. Instead of thinking of it as just a medical problem to be solved, we can own the experience for ourselves. We can take a stance that says I'm willing to be transformed by this thing I didn't ask for and I don't want – and in so doing we find meaning. You become the heroine of your own story.

it's deeply mystical – which is not at all the same as being spiritual or religious. It's not rational or logical, and I can't even explain what it is, but I know without a doubt that there is more to this world than the eye can see. And I know that when we feel utterly lost, when we're scared and we feel abandoned by life, there is a divine grace that shows up for us – if we're open to it. It becomes a source of superhuman courage and extraordinary love in the darkness. Even in all of this there is great beauty – a window into our humanity and the secrets of the cosmos that we can usually only perceive when our backs are against the wall.

So yes, cancer is shit. And there is also beauty, grace, and love.

I wish I could write like the great Sufi poets, but I haven't been given those gifts. I hope that what I lack in writing skills and talent I make up for in other ways.

May it be a source of inspiration and a balm for your soul. May it put wind beneath your wings.

Take what is useful, ignore what isn't.

DISCLAIMERS

I'm not a doctor, I have no medical qualifications, and I'm not giving advice or making recommendations about breast cancer treatment. If you have questions or concerns, talk to your medical team and/or do your own research. There's swearing and breasts in the book. If you're offended by either this isn't the book for you.

In documenting my own naked truth
my aim is to honour yours
may it be a source of inspiration
and a balm for your soul
may it put wind beneath your
wings
and light the path when it
feels as if all is lost

Be the Heroine of your
own Journey

Jane
X

13

Global Breast Cancer Stats

1. There were a reported **2.3m** women diagnosed worldwide with breast cancer in 2020.

3. By the end of 2020 there were **7.8m** women alive who were diagnosed in the past 5 years making breast cancer **the world's most prevalent cancer.**

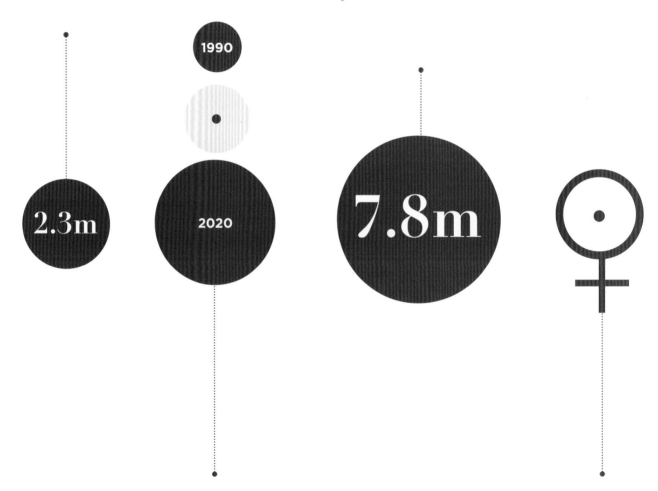

2. Over the past three decades, the number of **breast cancer diagnoses in the world has doubled.** While global incidence is rising it is complex to tease out the factors responsible for this including **changes in lifestyle and reproductive choices** worldwide, combined with significant **improvements in surveillance, screening and reporting.**

4. There are **more lost disability-adjusted life years (DALYs) by women to breast cancer** globally than any other type of cancer. It is THE most common cancer type diagnosed in women.

Global Data Source: World Health Organisation

5. Breast cancer is the leading cause of cancer death in women worldwide. Approximately **685,000 deaths in 2020.**

685,000

6. When **diagnosed and treated** at its earliest stages breast cancer **survival rates can be very high.**

Note: Survival rates are calculated at population level based on how far the cancer has spread, but your individual age, overall health, how well the cancer responds to treatment, the tumour grade at diagnosis, the presence of hormonal and genetic factors, and many other factors can also affect your outlook.

Risk factors for Breast Cancer include: being female, ageing, lifestyle factors such as weight, exercise and alcohol use, medical and reproductive factors, and family history.

	Most common cancer type diagnosed in women?	Number of women diagnosed (annual)	Lifetime risk	Deaths (annual) where known	Survival rate 5 years after diagnosis where known
AUS	2nd After Skin cancer	20,000 (Est. 2020)	1 in 8 Before age 85	3,034 (2018)	91%
UK	Yes	54,700 (2017)	1 in 7	11,500 (2018)	85%
US	2nd After skin cancer	282,000 (2021)	1 in 8	43,600 (2021)	89%
SING	Yes	2,200+	1 in 14 Before age 75	400+ Each year	80%
HK	Yes	4,600+ (2018)	1 in 14 Before age 75	735 (2018)	Not availble
GLOBAL	Yes	2.3m (2020)	Not availble	685,000 (2020)	Not availble

Breast cancer is the world's most prevalent cancer

TREAT

MENT

Something is wrong

Out of nowhere I get an anxiety attack. It was the 8th of September 2019 – I know because I happened to post about it on Instagram. Have never had them before. This first one is when I'm out in my neighbourhood walking my dogs after a lovely breakfast with a friend. Nothing is unsafe, nothing is out of the ordinary. It doesn't make sense.

Over the coming weeks they get worse and worse. In the bath, in bed when I'm about to fall off to sleep, even when I'm meditating. They're not related to feelings of safety: meditation/bath/bed are all my happy places.

I've never had them before. I don't know what to do. I think I'm losing my mind. They fill me with terror – I feel that I might die.

I see my doctor. We both think it's a combination of onset of menopause and anaemia.

Even though my periods are regular I'm at the right age for menopause. I've been on very low levels of HRT for a couple of years to regulate my hormones because they had started to drop at around 48. My iron is really low. I've always struggled a bit with it, but now it's worse. I'm anaemic.

He ups my HRT and it makes a minor difference. Minor. And I have an iron infusion. I collapse afterwards in the taxi home, which is quite scary, and almost go to the hospital as an emergency.

I decide to go home and lie down instead. I feel horrible for days. But it does make a small difference.

After several panicked calls, the doctor thinks I might need to see a cardiologist because the heart palpitations are so bad. My instinct is that this isn't the problem, but I don't know what is.

I'm anxious every moment of every day. I can't leave my house. I'm a prisoner to the anxiety.

I start taking valium the moment I wake up. It helps. And I have a couple of friends on speed dial who I call to calm me down when I think I'm about to die.

I have a small lump in my right breast. I've had it for months. I don't remember how I first realised it was there, probably because I didn't think anything of it at first. Women have lumps all the time and they come and go. But this one isn't going, it's getting bigger and more firm.

I have it examined and he tells me it's fine, nothing to worry about. But my instinct tells me to go for a mammogram. It would be my first one, having just turned 50.

I book a mammogram and go for the appointment on 15th October. The lovely woman who does my mammogram says "I'm sorry this is uncomfortable, these machines were probably invented by a man."

At this point I don't connect the anxiety attacks to the lump.

Something is very wrong

Powerlifting is my thing – I love it. I love training, I love competing.

I hold a couple of Australian records (Masters) and for several years have been focussed on getting strong enough for world records. I've been working towards a 160KG deadlift.

I entered this comp because it's an opportunity to have an attempt at a world record.

My anxiety is so bad I need someone to come to the ladies toilet with me every time I need to pee. The toilets are full of bodybuilders doing make-up and tan. On the platform the best deadlift I can manage – and it nearly killed me – is 143KG. It's a rubbish lift, and nowhere near the world record I wanted, but it's an Australian record so I'll take it.

It doesn't make sense. I can normally do 15 reps of that weight and today I can barely lift 1.

Something is wrong but I'm not joining the dots yet. I can't work it out.

In spite of the disappointment at my performance, this is one of the BEST days of my life.

AUSTRALIAN MASTERS RECORD: 143KG

I get my mammogram results – and something *is* wrong

Ref ID: 1182342

Dear Ms Marshall

Following your visit to our breast screening centre we would like to invite you back for further tests to clarify changes seen on your screening mammogram.

Read more about your assessment visit.

In most cases women who are called back are found not to have breast cancer.

"In most cases women who are called back are found not to have breast cancer".
I knew.
One of those quiet knowings that you don't verbalise because it will make it real.

I'm moving interstate for work

I've taken a contract for a year in Canberra and so I'm packing up my home in Melbourne, renting out my house, and taking the dogs. I'm not sure how I'm going to manage it with the crippling anxiety, but it's happening.

Before I go I've booked my annual visit to my spiritual teacher in Hong Kong. It's something I've been doing for years and this year I'm desperate for it – I'm hoping there's a spiritual answer to the anxiety that she can help me with.

My anxiety is so bad I have a friend stay on the phone with me all the way – from leaving my house in a taxi to the airport, all the way through check in, as I'm waiting in the lounge, as I'm boarding, and as I'm getting ready to take off. I let her go at the very last moment – as the stewardesses are coming round with that stern voice that says I've already told you once to switch off the phone and this time I really mean it.

My teacher meets me at the airport in Hong Kong so I don't have to do the train journey into the city on my own.

After the couple of days with my teacher I fly straight from Hong Kong to Canberra to start my new contract. Now I'm in a strange town, a place I've never been to before, and where I know no-one. I'm living out of boxes.

My anxiety is awful. I'm anxious EVERY MOMENT OF EVERY DAY and taking valium the moment I get up, more when I have to leave and go into the outside world, and more when I have to perform at work.

I think it's either the worst menopause ever or that my spiritual practice isn't strong enough and I'm failing somehow. I still don't connect the anxiety to the lump.

I go for my callback

I go for my callback today.

Everyone said 'oh I had a callback on my mammogram too, and it was fine, it'll just be a cyst'. But I knew.

It's why the nerves came this morning. I wore a pretty dress to make myself feel better.

I did the full suite of tests and was offered the chance to have the results before Christmas. I turned it down because I knew.

And there was no point knowing for 2 weeks when you can't actually do anything about it.

I have always thought I would get cancer one day on account of all the anger I used to have.

LOOKING BACK

Now I know what I know I'll be wondering forever if things could have been different or easier if I'd gone to see about the lump sooner. It's generally accepted that the earlier the diagnosis, the better the prognosis.

Maybe the cancer wouldn't have progressed so far by the time I got into treatment. And maybe I wouldn't have needed chemo.

People have said to me "you can't possibly have known", but I absolutely did know. Women have an instinct for knowing when something changes in our body. I only wish I'd listened sooner.

Survival rates are significantly higher with early detection

THE POINT IS — IF YOU HAVE A LUMP, OR ANY OTHER SIGNS OF BREAST CANCER, OR IF YOU JUST KNOW THAT SOMETHING IS WRONG, DON'T WAIT TO GET IT CHECKED

I HAVE BRE

I came home to Melbourne for Christmas for 2 weeks, due to be back in Canberra to start work again on 6 Jan. But I end up staying on and working from here because of the awful fires.

I was due to get my results in Canberra in person but as I'm not there I call and ask them to give them to me over the phone instead. I don't expect for one minute they're going to agree to do this, and expect to come off the phone with no news.

But they do, and minutes later I'm hearing the words "you have breast cancer".

Followed by "but it's a good cancer".

My first question: What is the survival rate? She explains that 'good' cancer means 90% of women are alive in 5 years.

She wants me to understand that I'm not likely to die. I hear a voice in my head saying but there's always someone who's in the 10%...

My second question: If I need chemo is it the kind of chemo where I will lose all my hair? Yes. Interesting that I went straight there, to the idea that I don't want to lose my hair. I like my hair.

I start pondering whether I would be brave enough to be bald or whether I would go the wig route. There's some cool wigs these days.

Third question: Can I keep working? Maybe. This is a big one for me because when you're single there's only you paying the bills.

I get practical right away.

Within 5 minutes I had spoken to my private medical insurers to make sure I was up to date.

Within an hour I had an appointment with a surgeon and instructions to get the set of blood tests that would be needed.

I have to come off my HRT – today, right now – because it feeds the cancer. But the HRT is one of the things I'm using to manage my anxiety – what's going to happen when I stop taking it? I'm actually terrified to come off it. If the anxiety gets any worse than it is I wouldn't be able to work. I wouldn't be able to leave my house. Can I just take more valium?

I have cancer. It doesn't make sense.

AST CANCER

Final Result of Assessment Visit: Malignant lesion

Assessment Recommendation: Treatment

Assessment Comments: 17/12/2019 [redacted] (Radiologist)

Jane was recalled to further assess a stellate mass detected in her right breast on screening mammogram performed at BreastScreen Victoria.

Breast density is visually graded as BI-RADS D - The breasts are extremely dense which lowers the sensitivity of mammography.

Further workup with mammographic tomosynthesis and ultrasound confirmed the presence of a 16 x 9 x 14mm malignant mass at the 6 o-clock radius of the right breast, 7cm FN. Small foci of intra-lesional calcification noted on mammogram. No axillary lymphadenopathy.

Ultrasound guided core biopsy performed.

[redacted] Clinical Coordinator 19.12.2019:
The pathology result from the Core biopsy of the lesion shows invasive lobular carcinoma, predicted grade 2.

The client has been given this result verbally as she is currently in Melbourne. She will see her GP in Melbourne to arrange appropriate surgical and oncology work up.

At the surgeon already

I'm already at the surgeon 2 days after diagnosis because that's the kind of person I am.

I want this dealt with asap. I want this thing out of my body. And practically – I'm a consultant – if I don't work I don't get paid. I can't afford too much downtime.

A lot of people in Melbourne know the pink door of Chantel Thornton: Super-surgeon for breast cancer. And she sees you fast.

I don't know anything about breast cancer.

She talks about lots of things I can't wrap my head around and I'm learning lots of new words. The word 'invasive' comes up a lot.

The good news – I can work through both radio and chemo. And we caught it early. The news I didn't like so much – we may already be at stage 3 rather than stage 2 – my angry cells are possibly fast-moving.

But even worse than that: I'll be on medication for 5–10 years that depresses your oestrogen and gives you the worst kind of menopause.

Having surreal conversations about mastectomies. And a total stranger is taking photos of my breasts.

They make a BIG point about advising me not to go anywhere near Dr Google. Facing the reality that none of this is going to be exactly cheap.

It all feels weird.

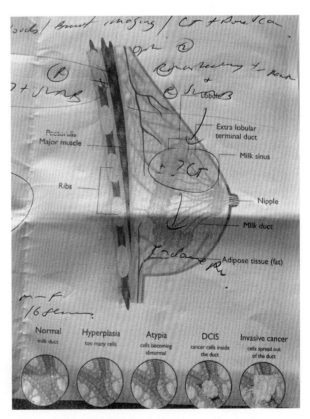

Notes from my surgeon

29

9 JAN 2020

Pre–op tests

Today was a full-on day. I had another mammogram, ultrasound, blood tests, a CT scan, and two different machines that looked for cancer in my bones.

The mammograms and ultrasound were a breeze – I've done both of those tests already recently so I was pretty blasé about them. But when I got to the CT scan something clicked. I started to realise all this was actually happening. I got claustrophobia, anxiety, and started hyperventilating. I wasn't very brave. There was a lovely nurse who held my hand while I had a few tears. In fact everyone at the hospital was lovely.

Today was definitely the day that shit got real. I really have cancer.

It was probably 8 hours all up. I went home exhausted and felt as sick as a parrot. Really really sick. I crawled straight into bed.

12 38 31

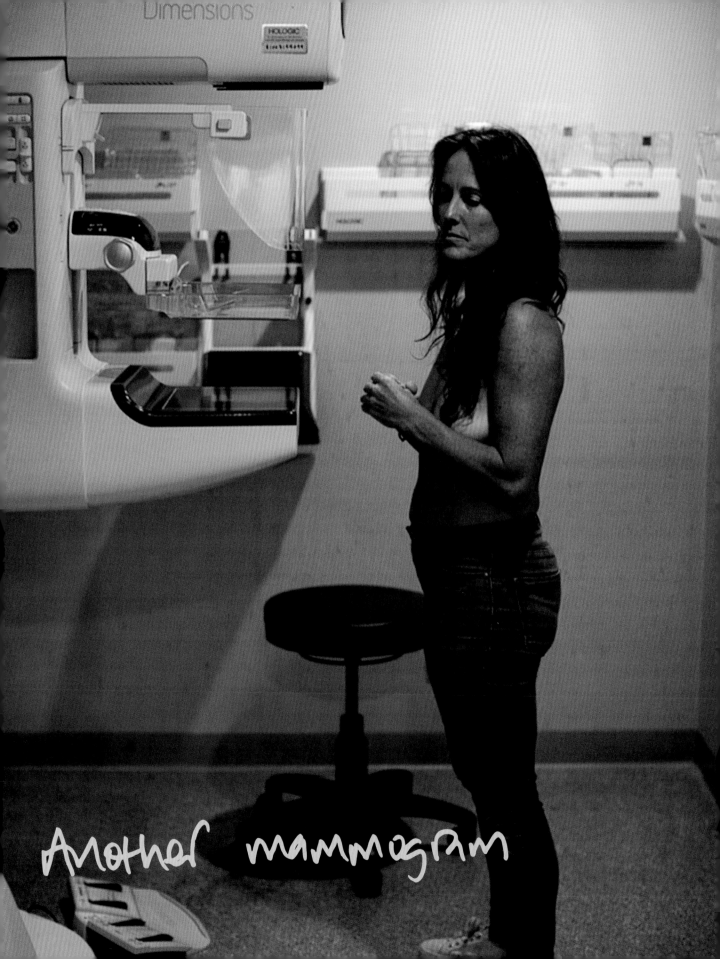

Another mammogram

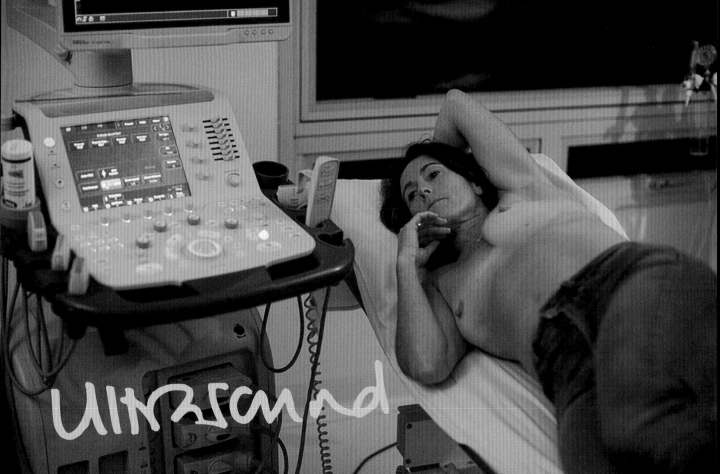

Ultrasound

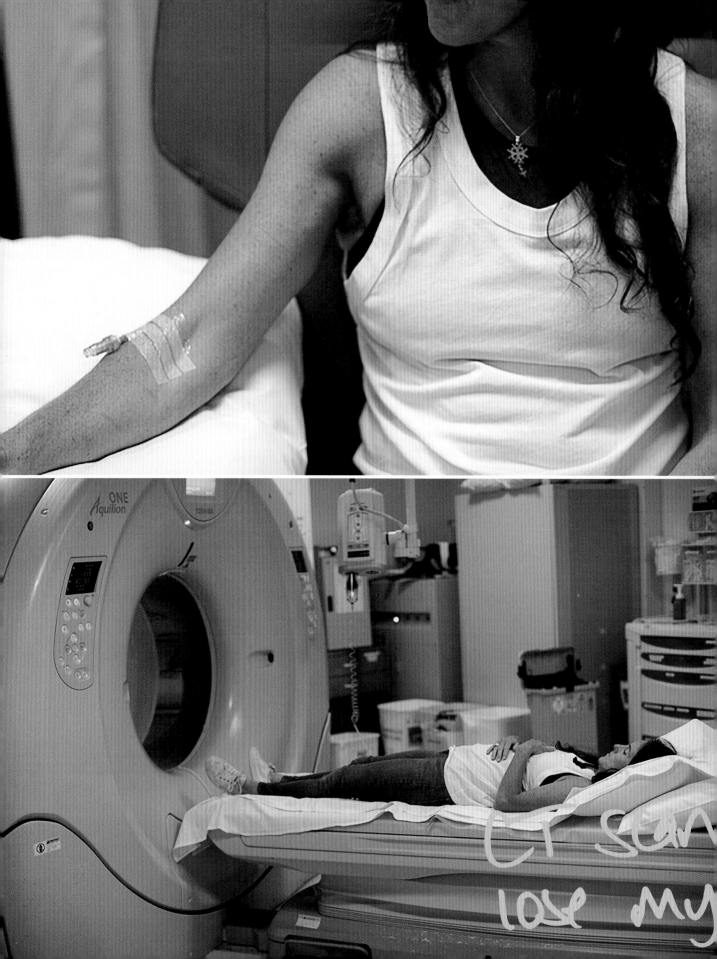

CT scan
lose my

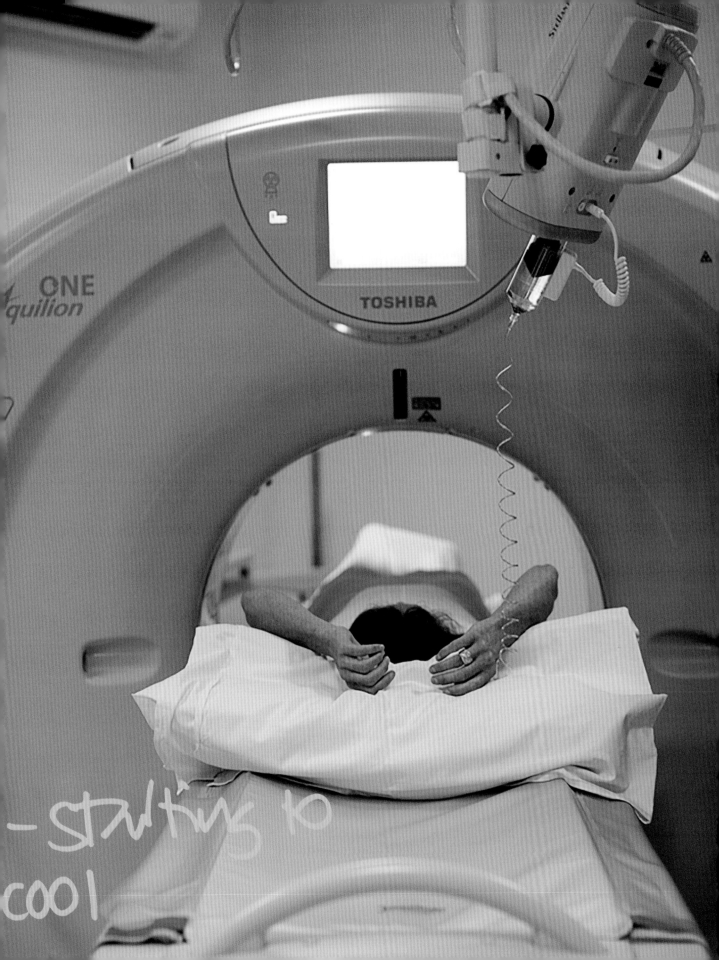

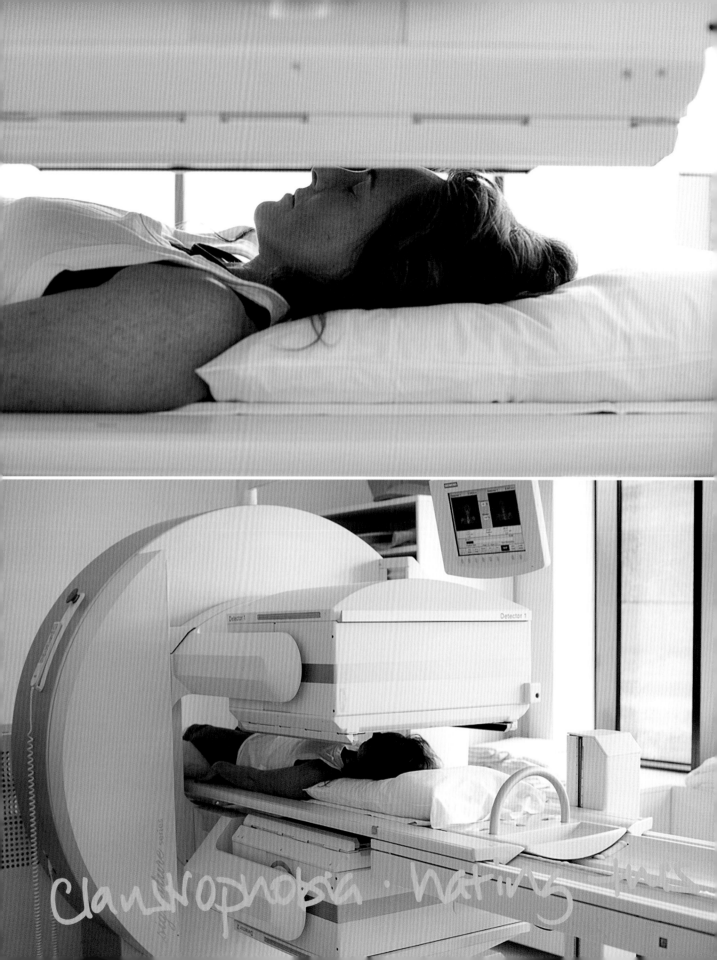

Claustrophobia · Waiting

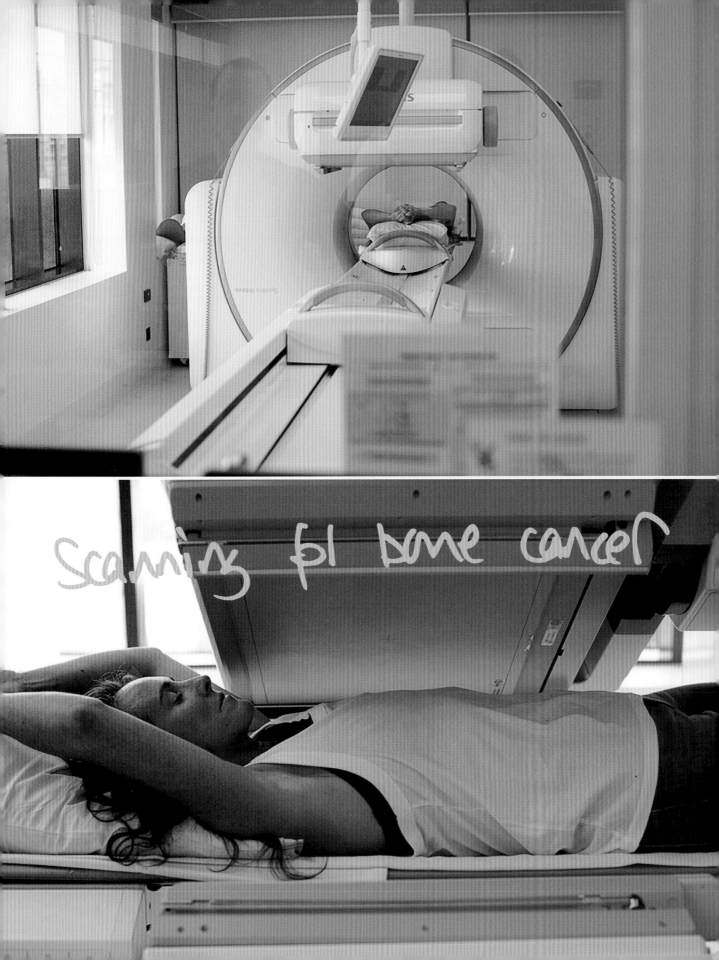

scanning for bone cancer

Anxiety attack

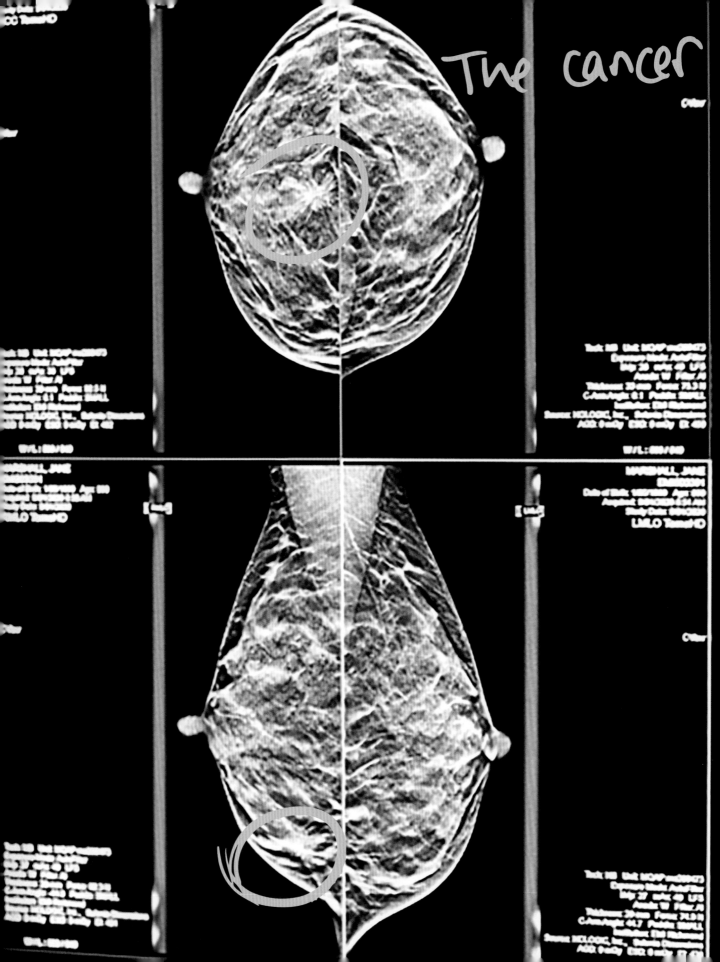

9 JAN 2020
OK friends...

OK FRIENDS...I have breast cancer. Feels weird to be writing this, and a part of my brain is telling me not to, because what if it's not actually true – but I'm booked in for an operation on Monday 20th, so I think it probably is. Also feels weird to be sharing it on social media, but as so many of you were so kind when I went for tests before Christmas, I felt like I needed to close the circle. Won't know about treatment until after the op. I'm not going to die, and much goodness will come from this experience, as is always the case with these things. It's all good. Love x

12   88   157

All the emotions in four days

The emotional side to this is a complete fucking rollercoaster. I found out a few days ago and in those days I've had every human emotion it's possible to have. I wake up every day feeling something different.

The first day there were lots of tears. I don't think for a second that I'm going to die. It was just the shock.

For a couple of days after that I got really practical – I've had intense bouts of mania, where I couldn't sit still and needed to be really busy. While the mania was a bit uncomfortable and exhausting, it was also incredibly productive: there's a lot to do to get ready for an operation.

I keep waking up at 3am, I haven't slept properly for days.

Yesterday was pre-op tests and the first day that I felt fear. Dealing with the medical system when you're not used to it is something else. And the machines are awesome but terrifying.

I've also had terrible anxiety, and rage. I'm not aware of feeling angry about the fact that this has happened, it's just something that came through. I wanted to scream.

Interestingly I notice there's no self-pity: there's no woe is me or any of that. I feel very accepting – things happen to all of us, none of us is immune to life. It all just feels ok: I'll deal with it. I know it sounds cliched, but something good will come from this, I know it.

I've had moments of very deep peace. The most beautiful thing that's coming through is just so much love. I have so much tenderness towards myself, and so much love from others too. I feel myself becoming really soft.

I know that in the scheme of things it's not important but I'm really worried I'm going to lose my powerlifting.

Why did this happen to me?

No-one in my family, as far as I know, has breast cancer. My mum doesn't anyways.

I go through the possible reasons that this might have happened to me.

I've always thought that stress is a cause of cancer and I've been stressed-as-a-lifestyle-choice for a long time. I work way too hard and put myself under way too much pressure. I burnt out 10 years ago. Have I stressed myself to death?

I was depressed and angry for a long time when I was young too. I have memories of myself thinking that this would give me cancer one day.

I've heard women who have had breast cancer say that it came shortly after a very stressful period in their lives, and I did have some drama in my personal life the last few years. Perhaps this triggered it.

My cancer feeds on hormones. I was on HRT for a while, and I took the pill for a really really long time. It helped with my horrible periods and we all wanted condom-free sex when I was young. I'll be pissed off if it was this, I hardly had any sex anyway, and most of it wasn't that great. I realise that my hormones have been out of whack my whole life and this must have had something to do with it.

I think about one of the spiritual teachers that I follow – she talks about how the universe is impersonal, but we humans take everything so personally. So why not me? We all get ill and die one day. Maybe it's just a random mystery.

Or maybe it was something else that I can't see or understand yet.

I talk to the cancer and ask her what she wants to say to me. There's anger. Or what feels like anger.

IF YOU HAVE CANCER, SOMETHING NEEDS TO CHANGE, SURELY. WHAT IS IT?

LOOKING BACK: I wrote in my diary that I felt Kali energy, the desire to destroy and be destroyed. I didn't know what that meant at the time. I do now, but I won't explain it here or it'll ruin the book. I was getting intense waves of this energy in my body for days. It was wild, completely visceral.

I'm not fighting or trying to beat cancer

I've noticed that a lot of language around cancer is language around 'fighting it' or 'beating it' and that's not how I'm feeling AT ALL.

I don't want to fight or beat anything.

Fighting something takes a lot of energy. I've spent my life fighting and I've got no fight in me any more.

I feel that for me the point is to stop fighting.

And I can't change this so why fight it.

It also doesn't make sense to me to fight a thing that isn't separate to me but is literally inside me. That would be fighting myself. It doesn't work for me to think about it that way.

I'm feeling something completely different. It's time to love myself more. I feel softness. All my instinct says that fighting won't help my body, but love will.

I think what people really mean when they say they want to fight it is that they want to get well, and to do this requires strength.

But I'm not fighting, I'm healing. There's something that needs to heal.

Is this a mistake?

Even though I'm booked for
surgery in a week, there's
a large part of me that still
thinks this is all just a big
mistake.

I don't believe it. I keep
expecting the doctors to call
and tell me that they haven't
found any cancer after all.

I keep hoping that maybe I
could still go back to living
my life as I did before.

But they called today and I
asked if they were sure about
all of this and things haven't
changed.

I still have cancer.

For after diagnosis

 Buy a journal and write down everything you're thinking and feeling. It'll help you to process the thing later to have this to look back on.

 Write down everything related to your medical treatment. Write down your questions before appointments, and record all your conversations with your medical team. You won't be able to hold it in memory.

 Have a (calm) friend who comes to every medical appointment with you. To help you ask questions and record/remember answers, and to help you manage your emotional state.

 Make your bedroom/home a place you enjoy being. Buy new bedding (linen is best for menopause).

 If you have questions ask the breast cancer nurses. In my experience they're gorgeous women, and there's nothing they haven't seen before.

 Make a couple of playlists for mood and energy. Make one for relaxation/managing stress and one for improving your mood.

 Your immune system is having to work very very hard during cancer, particularly during chemo: do what you can to support it. Sleep, laughter, love. Avoid stress. Eat loads of fruit and veg. Make sure you keep your vitamin C levels up. Get vitamin D from sunshine if you can bear it (chemo sometimes makes bearing sunshine hard) and if not supplement.

155KG deadlift

I felt like screaming. So I deadlifted.

I've been chasing a 160KG world record all year, and haven't made it yet.

I'm gutted at the idea that I might not be able to powerlift after this. So in case this is the last time I lift anything really fucking heavy again I went to the gym today and did this. I've only ever lifted 155KG once before. All things considered I'm pretty happy that I was still able to do it.

It got a ton of emotions out.

Day before surgery

Procrastination: When you should be packing a hospital bag and doing serious adult stuff and you think nah, I'm going to lie in the sun instead.

18   26   14

My mum

My mum worries.
I decided not to tell her I was going in for surgery.

The night before I changed my mind and called her. In case I
died on the operating table I thought it would be cruel not to
have called her.

She did that thing that mums do. She's sobbing.

I love her but in the end I have to tell her "I'm putting the
phone down now mum I can't do this".

I don't have the wherewithal to hold her up and me.
We communicate through my sister for the next little while.

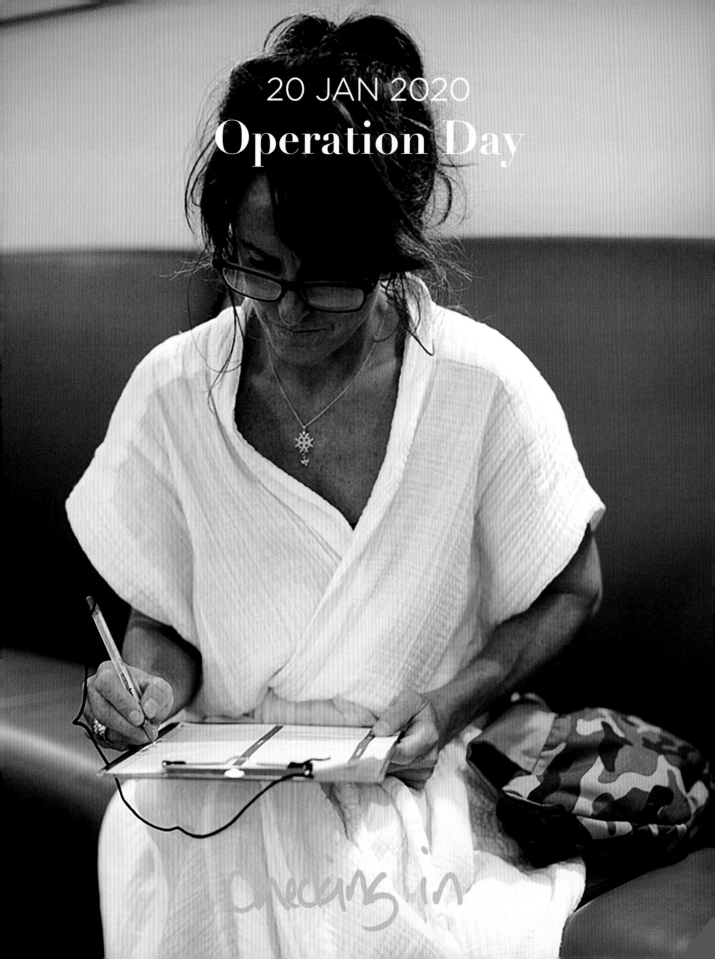

20 JAN 2020
Operation Day

checking in

My lucky socks which went with me to every appointment

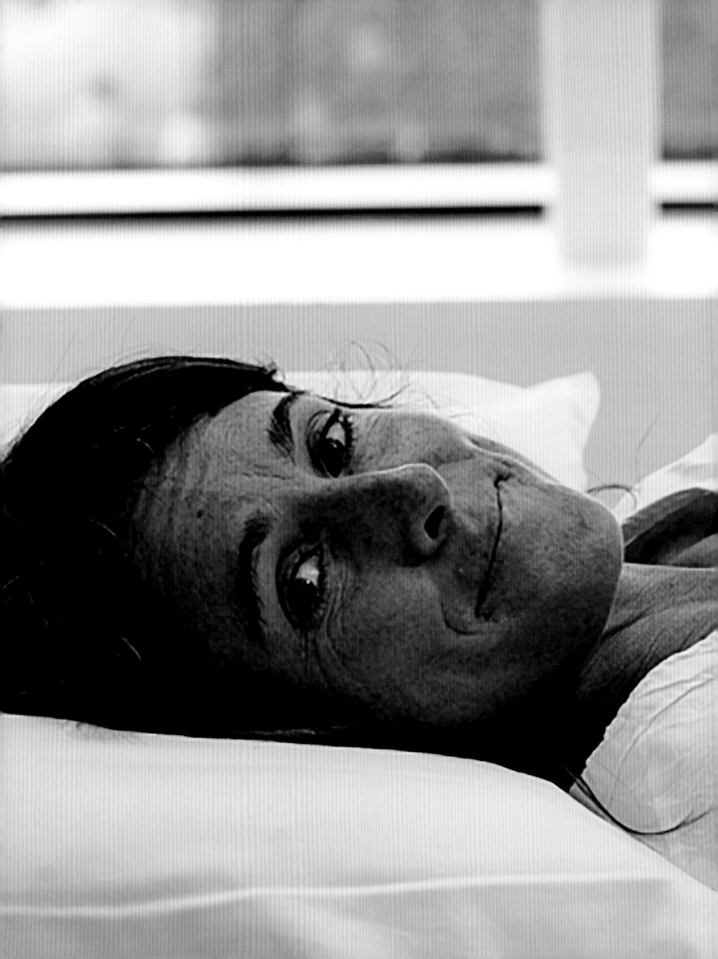

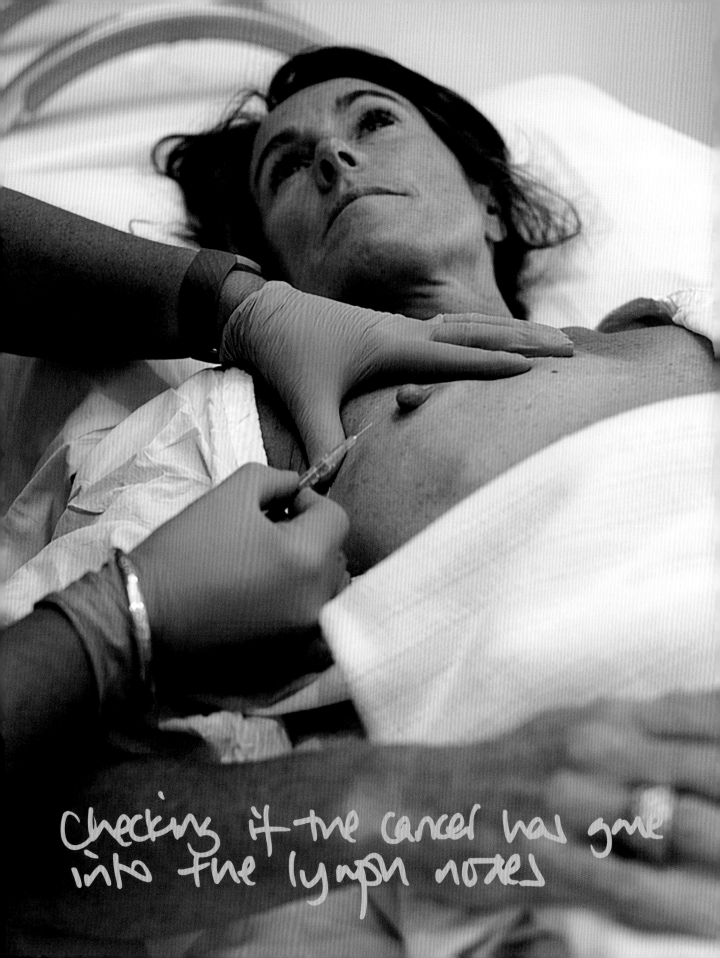

Checking if the cancer had gone into the lymph nodes

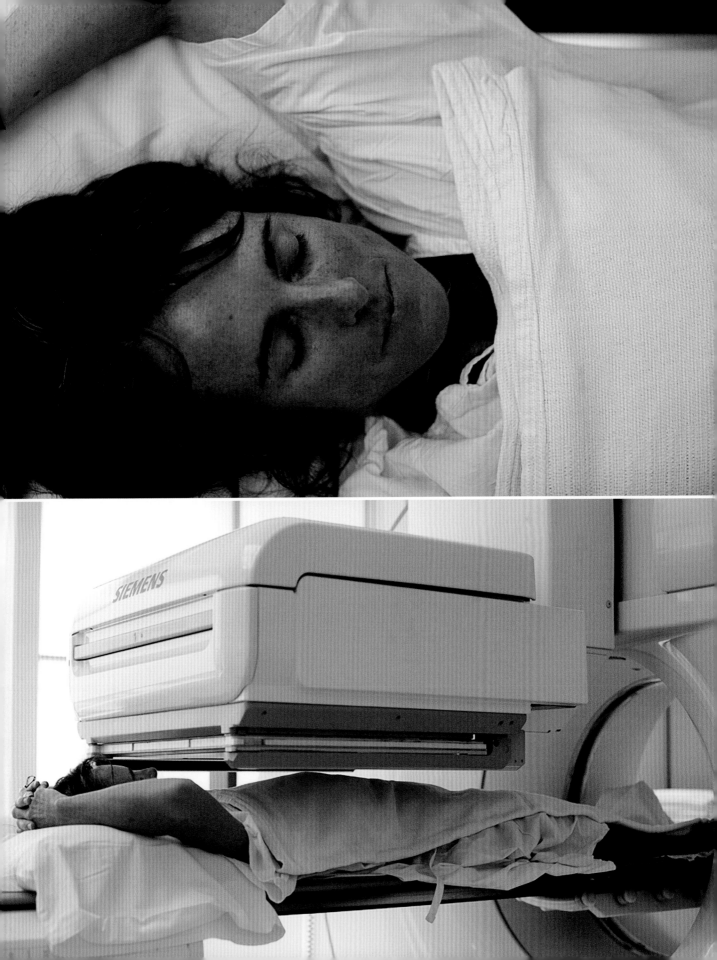

Nervous

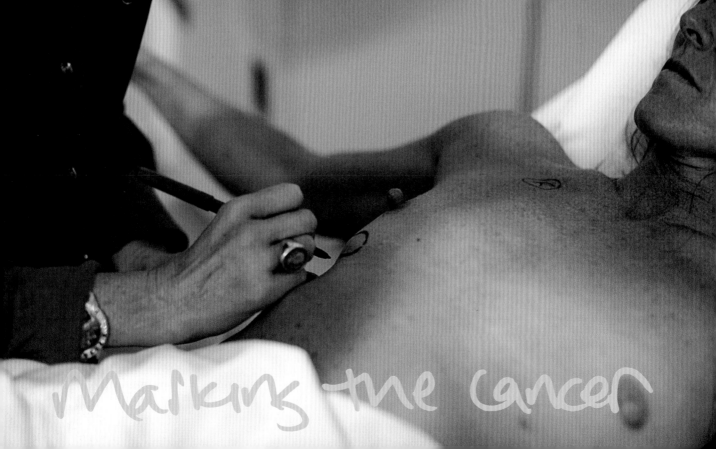

marking the cancer

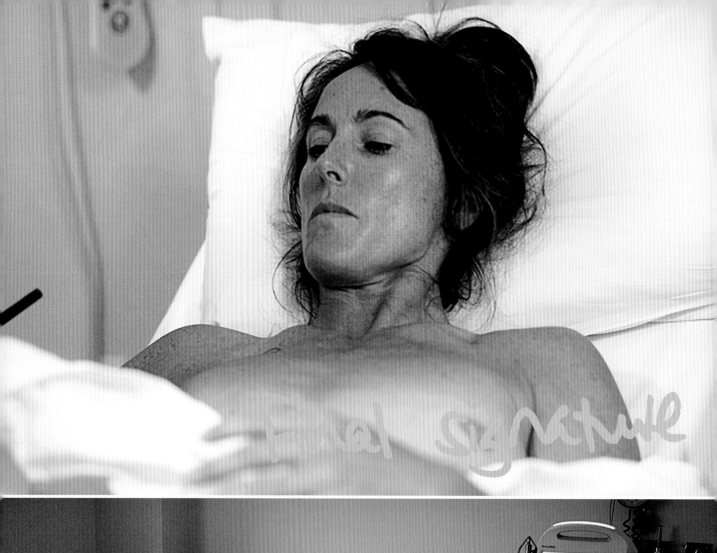

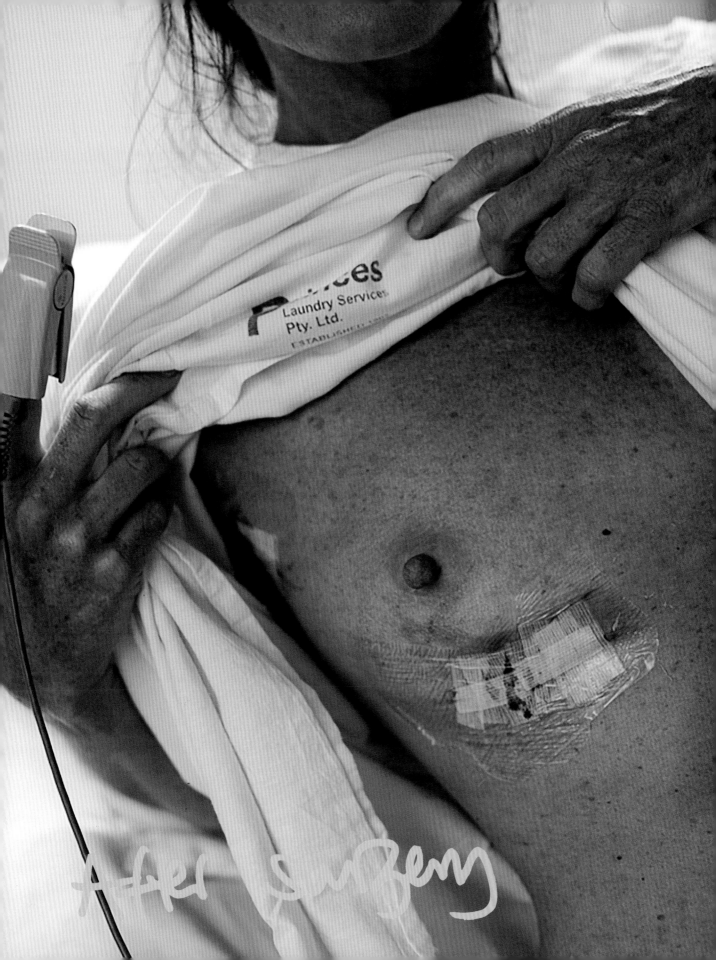

After Surgery

21 JAN 2020
The morning after surgery

Feel like I've been run over by a truck this morning.

I woke up miserable – huge adrenalin and anaesthetic comedown, plus being on your own in a hospital room is kinda lonely.

So I went in search of coffee and then I danced myself happy.

At home the day after surgery

These pictures make me laugh at how little I knew.
I had just done my first surgery and came home feeling fantastic.
We drank wine and had fish and chips.

Allowed the dogs on the table!
(I never do this.)

There was a party atmosphere – that happy chaos when you're out of your routine and not working and friends are over.
I did cancer!

I had no idea what was coming.

I hadn't ever seen friends or family go through it.

No idea at all.

I HAD NO IDEA WHAT WAS COMING

My Cancer

So this is what they took out of my breast. I love that my surgeon gave me this – "it's for your blog" she said.

And this is the scan of the cancer. (Below)

I find these pictures fascinating. I come back to them all the time. I love being able to see inside the body. I look at them and realise that the cancer is in me, it's cells gone rogue, it's not something I'm fighting.

Right Breast
60C 8cmFN

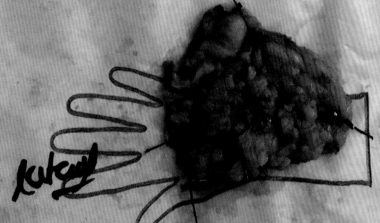

63

Not the best news

When you plan on going to get your post-surgery results on your own, and then you realise that's a really dumb idea and call a friend who drops everything at 5 minutes notice to show up for you... @lisarenkin

2   37   30

The cancer is in a lymph node in the right armpit already which means they need to go back in and take out all the lymph nodes in the area. I'll be back in within a week. They have to move fast because they go back into the same wound in the armpit and they have to get in before it starts healing. I'm pretty grumpy about a second surgery. I'm bouncing back really fast from the first surgery, and no-one warned me that a second one was a possible scenario. Two surgeries in one week feels like a lot. I find it incredibly frustrating to

not know the full picture of what might happen - I'm not sure if it's because they think you can't handle it or if they don't know either. Also conversations about chemo ramping up. It's looking more likely. I'm gutted. I totally hate the idea of it.

On the other hand I'm bouncing back really fast from the first surgery. I don't look awful at all, there's already some life back in my face.

How I feel today

I asked Rochelle to take some photos. Not altogether sure why. I was feeling a bit defiant. Not sure what of.

I think I look blank. I published this photo. Not sure why I did that either.

One of my friends said it was confronting. But there are sexualised women's breasts everywhere no?

So what's the problem with this image?

Back in the gym

5 days after my first surgery and back in the gym but doing really really light weights to protect the 2 wounds.

I feel better when I move, it makes me happy.

Actually none of it hurt.

I won't be competing for a while, so it's a good year to take all the heavy weights off and work on technique.

My squats have always been horrible anyway.

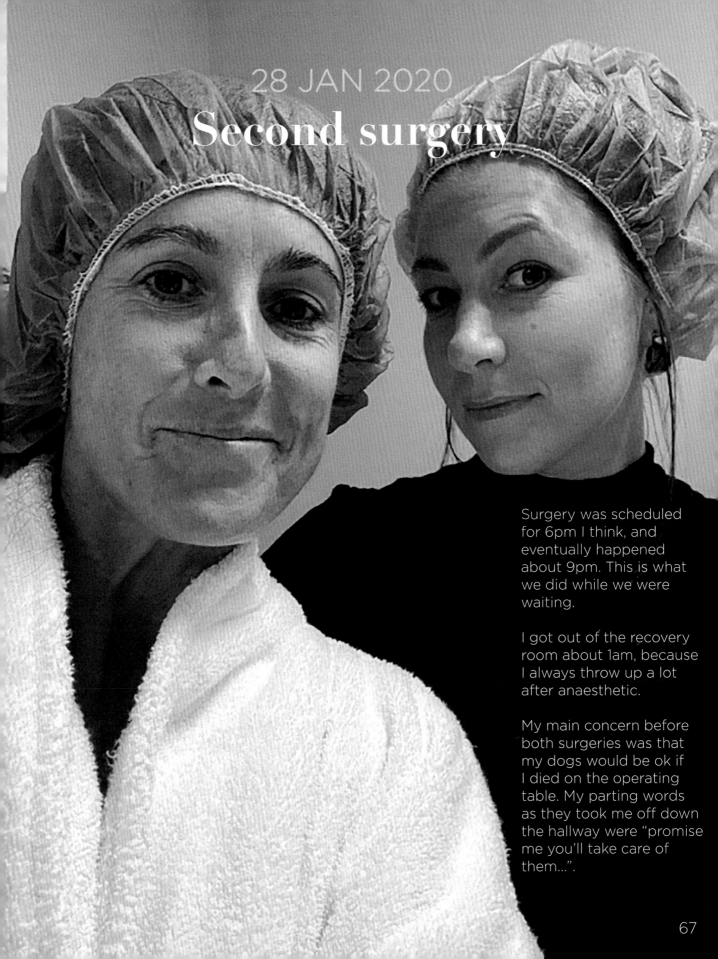

Second surgery

Surgery was scheduled for 6pm I think, and eventually happened about 9pm. This is what we did while we were waiting.

I got out of the recovery room about 1am, because I always throw up a lot after anaesthetic.

My main concern before both surgeries was that my dogs would be ok if I died on the operating table. My parting words as they took me off down the hallway were "promise me you'll take care of them...".

The morning after surgery 2

This is me feeling like I want to die. Surgery 2 was so much harder than surgery 1.

I had used up a lot of adrenalin for the first one – not knowing there might be a second one – and not knowing I had to keep anything in the tank for later. And I didn't get out of surgery until 1am – late start, plus I always vomit a lot after anaesthetic.

Then they kept waking me up in the night – to make me walk and go to the bathroom. But I couldn't. I would manage a few steps, cry, and stumble back to bed. The nurse wasn't happy with me about that. I felt like I was disappointing her but I'm not really sure what they expected.

I couldn't stomach coffee in the morning – THAT'S HOW BAD I WAS. I wanted to go home so badly I lied. I said I was fine. I made myself walk to the bathroom to show I was fine. But I couldn't put my own clothes on, I couldn't look up because I felt so sick, I couldn't focus on anything. There was no way I was going to be able to walk out of the hospital – I needed a wheelchair.

Humiliating. But I just wanted out of that place.

In the car on the way home I was holding in vomit the whole journey – facing ahead, window open to get as much fresh air as possible. Cursing every red traffic light. Just keep facing forward. Just keep facing forward. The second the car stopped at home I fell out and threw up all over my driveway.

I did wonder for a while if I'd made a terrible mistake and whether I should really be in a hospital.

But being at home, daytime napping in my own bed with the dogs, made me feel so much better. By the afternoon I was out walking the dogs in my favourite park. The body is amazing.

Draining the lymph nodes

I had to bring this baby home.

It's sewn into my armpit for at least a week to drain the lymph nodes.

I hate it already.

It's not just the drainage, my body is pissed off about another surgery in the same armpit wound. She feels brutalised.

We are at a low ebb today.

My armpit hurts like hell, I can hardly sleep because it's sewn into my armpit, and it wakes me up every time I move.

The pain killers don't work and they make you feel sick and give you constipation. I can't put clothes on or off or reach my hair because it hurts to move my right arm.

I'm only eating because friends are bringing me food.

I'm really really grumpy.

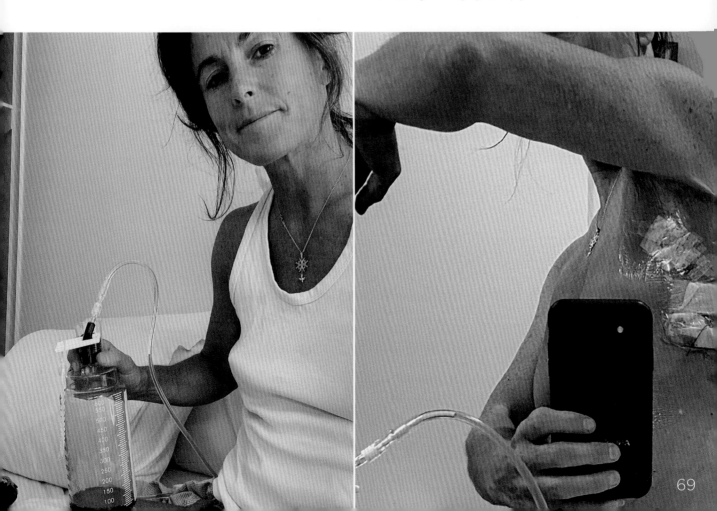

Graham

Graham called me on Thursday and said GIVE ME SOMETHING TO DO so I said ok, want to be my emotional support animal for when I go get my results? (Analysis of the lymph nodes they just took out during second surgery.)

He ended up spending his whole Friday evening with me at the surgeon's office.

Honestly, I think he liked the captive audience and is secretly hoping I have to have chemo so that he has someone to perform for who can't get away (cancer brings on a weird humour people, roll with it).

And he bought me ice-cream while we waited.

So the news is that there was no more cancer in the lymph nodes they just took out, which is great, but the kind of cancer that it was indicates it might be aggressive so may still need chemo, which I've been desperate to avoid.

The best news is that me and my drainage bottle broke up last night so I'm no longer in any pain and I'm going lifting this morning.

So much love @aussieartnow

15   40   31

I DIDN'T REALLY KNOW GRAHAM WELL BEFORE THIS. I WAS FRIENDS WITH HIS HUSBAND. HE LITERALLY CALLED OUT OF THE BLUE TO OFFER HELP, AND TURNED OUT TO BE THE BEST FRIEND A GIRL WITH CANCER COULD WISH FOR. HE CALLED ME AT 6PM EVERY SINGLE NIGHT — ALL YEAR — TO MAKE SURE I WAS OK.

Squats

The surgery this week was brutal, and I thought it might have finished me off for a while, but within a couple of days the wound was healing quickly and I really needed to move. It makes me happy and I'm convinced that being happy is the best thing you can do for your immune system.

So back to training as usual – and somehow managed to pull out the bag my best squats ever. Don't have full range of motion on my right arm yet because the wound in my armpit is still pretty sore, so we used a 20KG bag instead of a bar. My surgeon said I could lift 10KG, but I figured she meant 10KG on each side.

Went home and slept for about 4 hours, but very happy indeed.

19   42   17

THE POWERLIFTING DRAGON LIVES TO FIGHT ANOTHER DAY

7 FEB 2020
Stitches out and DEXA scan

The dressing is off and I felt the lymph node scar for the first time. This is me asking "when can I deadlift again?". Not joking.

Look at my scars. I'm amazed at how quickly the body heals.

The surgeon is happy with her needlework.

After this I go for a DEXA scan. They want to start hammering me with chemo and then give me hormone blockers to turn off the supply of food for the cancer. This creates a bone density risk. So – a scan of the bones. Rochelle and I both agreed the machine was a bit lame compared to all the other machines we've been dealing with. Most disappointing.

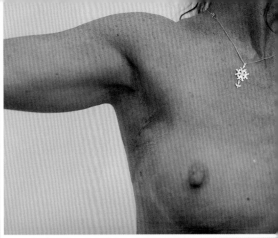
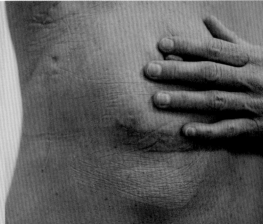

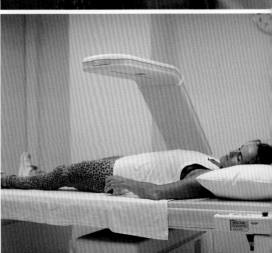

The day I deadlifted 90KG

11 days after second surgery.

I was told by my surgeon to lift no more than 10 KG.

I'm not sure what to say. I had to do it.
It was only 1 rep.

I just needed to know if I was still in the game, so I could relax and not spend the next 6 months wondering.
I'm still in the game.

Really I wanted 100KG, but I heard a voice say that's enough. Well done to me for stopping before I hurt myself.
I never told my surgeon about this. Or anyone really.

Cording

Even though I can deadlift, I can hardly raise my right arm. I'm getting really stressed about it in case it's serious and it's always going to be like this.

A lovely friend Pam who specialises in this stuff gives me an awesome massage and my arm is moving tons better.

It's called cording apparently and a lot of it can be broken down with stretching or a good massage. It looks like its name – it's a tight cord that you can see.

It's cool to hear the popping when it cracks during massage too – and instant relief.

Also, once you've had lymph nodes out you have to learn about lymphoedema. The body needs time to develop new pathways to clear infections now.

Lymphatic drainage massage is good, and need to avoid infections/cuts.

After the session with my friend Pam my arms goes tight again and I'm completely stressed about it.

I start sessions with a breast cancer physio. She tells me it's all going to be fine and all she needs to do is massage it out. I burst into tears.

After just one session I have nearly full range of motion. When I walked in it barely moved. Sacha also gives me some great advice: "you're just going to have a shit year and then it gets better".

No-one had given me a timeframe before and I don't cope well when I don't know where the finish line is. This helps massively. Much happier.

TIPS FOR LYMPHOEDEMA

If you've had lymph node surgery read up on lymphoedema so you know what to do/not do.

Make sure to not get cuts or scratches in the affected arm.

Massage from an oncology specialist: to help the body to make new pathways for clearing.

Exercise, keeping moving, to keep the lymphatic system working.

Lumps in my thyroid

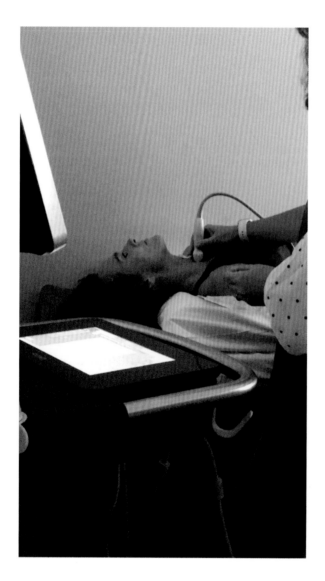

One of the problems when you have cancer is that now every single lump and body in your body, every single thing that feels off, every blood test that isn't quite right – it ALL needs to be investigated.

Just in case there's more cancer.

Being ill takes up so much time.

My pre-op tests showed something weird in my thyroid so now we're off to see if I have more cancer.

Spoiler – I don't.

First day back at work in Canberra

When you're doing your first work trip to Canberra since surgery and your gorgeous friend Therese Fitzpatrick is going back to New York (she's a total badass who runs a global programme for the UN #proudfriend) and you get to share a cab to the airport. Made a difficult morning absolutely delightful. Love also to @un_wife who waved us off.

6   35   131

LOOKING BACK

I'm smiling but I was feeling really really fragile. I did not want to leave my house. I didn't want to fly to another city and stay in an Airbnb alone. If I hadn't needed the money I wouldn't have done it.

I had to take lots of valium to make it. When I got there my client screamed at me – in hearing of a whole office of people.

There was no toughness left in me. I almost cried. I almost walked out and went straight to the airport home. But I didn't. Because that's not how women of my generation roll. We always get the job done.

27 FEB 2020
Happy

Feeling really really happy. First big week back into work and real life done. I made it.

It felt huge to me.

To get on a plane and go to another city where I have no friends and to still turn up and be brilliant for my client – when I was so tired and so fragile after the surgery, and while my brain is full of whether or not I'm going to do chemo.

I nailed it.

12   38   31

For being in hospital

 Really good headphones to listen to music and block out the energy of the place.

 A shawl/blanket to wrap yourself in, for warmth, but also for security.

 Essential oils to help with fear/anxiety.

 Have something lovely to wear that makes you feel good.

 Take your own coffee/tea/anything else you really like to have.

 Take chargers if you use lots of devices to occupy yourself.

 Don't do your nails. I know it's tempting to have a mani-pedi to make yourself feel better, but they need access to your nails to monitor your oxygen when you're under.

 Protect your energy. Hospitals are full of weird energy and entities, and there's a lot of fear. Protect your energy by erecting a strong bubble of protection around yourself.

Negotiating to avoid chemo

At the oncologist today discussing chemo. "It's the worst possible news Jane" is how my oncologist started this meeting. I wanted to avoid chemo if at all possible. Who wants chemo?

But the cancer had spread into a lymph node. Only 1, but that means it's already on the move from the original lump. Normally that means chemo is non-negotiable.

In my striving to avoid it I paid through the nose for the Prosigna test (not advertising it, just mentioning it) to check my likelihood of the cancer returning. My oncologist said if my score was lower than 10 we might be able to get away without it. My score was 65. Not even borderline.

So my statistical chance of recurrence within 10 years is 31%, compared to 10% average across all women who get breast cancer. Many now consider breast cancer to not be a death sentence, but a manageable disease. 31% is not good though.

But how do you interrogate this stuff? How much of a role do your genes play in illness versus say stress, exercise, and diet? No-one can tell you. How do you even make sense of these things? From the oncologist perspective, this is an unacceptably high risk ("if it comes back Jane it's automatically stage 4 and there is nothing I can do for you") and I leave with details of the chemo

she wants me to have starting in a few weeks.

I tell her I'm not 100% there yet. I have two weeks to decide. She's always allowed me to be the decision-maker and sees her job as laying out my options. She says I can let her know right up until the day.

I feel more sorry for my friend Graham than I do for myself. One minute it's all witty banter in the waiting room, the next he's having to sit and bear witness to a conversation about my dying. He looks like he's going to cry at the news. He's looking at me to check that I'm ok. I'm ok, quite calm really. I think I was feeling less awkward than he was.

We go and get cake and he helps me make plans for how I would be able to keep working – another major concern. One other thing: it's also the day I'm declared menopausal.

The day you officially get declared post-menopausal. Had to stop taking HRT because my cancer is strongly hormone receptor-positive. So this is it. On the other side.

MARSHALL, JANE		Lab		
DoB 01/05/1980		Test	FHP-0	
			Report	
SERUM HORMONES				
		FSH IU/L	LH IU/L	E2 pmol/L
Lab.No Date				
12941329 17/10/19		3	1	427
14762521 21/02/20		60	32	< 70
REFERENCE INTERVALS				
Follicular		1-6	1-10	70-530
Mid cycle		5-20	15-100	235-1300
Luteal		1-12	1-20	205-790
Pregnant (1st Trim.)		1-6	1-10	230-910
Post menopausal		>20	>20	0-120

prosigna

Patient	Specimen	Run Set ID: 2022170P
Tumor Size: <= 2cm	ID #: 354634748 JANE	Comments:
Lymph Nodes: node-positive (1-3	Date Reported: February 17, 2020	

 prosigna
Breast cancer
prognostic gene signature assay

ID #: 354634748 JANE, MARSHALL Tumor Size: <= 2cm   Lymph Nodes: node positive (1-3 nodes)

Assay Description: The Prosigna® breast cancer gene signature assay measures the expression of 50 different genes to identify subtype and report a Risk of Recurrence Score (ROR), which is used to assign the patient to a predefined risk group. These results are derived from a proprietary algorithm based on the PAM50 gene signature, intrinsic subtype, and clinical variables including tumor size and nodal status.

Risk of Recurrence*:

Low risk	Intermediate risk	High risk

0 —————————— **65** —————————— 100

Subtype: **luminal B**

* The ROR ranges from 0 through 100 and correlates with the probability of distant recurrence (DR) in the tested patient population. The risk classification is provided to guide the interpretation of the ROR using cutoffs related to clinical outcome.

Probability of Distant Recurrence:

In the clinical validation studies, patients who were node-positive (1-3 nodes), luminal B subtype, with an ROR score of 65 were in the high-risk group. This group a[...] distant recurrence at 10 years.

The Prosigna® algorithm has been validated by 2 randomized clinical trials including more than 2400 patients [...] these 2 clinical validation studies shows that the probability of distant recurrence for the high-risk populati[...]

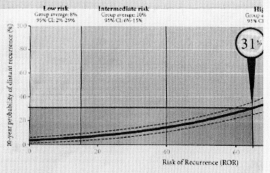

Low risk	Intermediate risk	High[...]
Group average 8%	Group average 16%	Group [...]
95% CI: 2%-29%	95% CI: 6%-15%	95% CI[...]

31%

10-year probability of distant recurrence (%) vs *Risk of Recurrence (ROR)*

For more information, visit PROSIGNA.com or e-mail info@pros[...]

[...]ta apply to patients being treated with hormone therapy for 5 years as in the tested patient population. See Package Ins[...]
[...]ent population. It is unknown whether these findings can be extended to other patient populations or treatment schedules[...]

< 10%

NanoString Technologies, Inc.   530 Fairview Avenue N │ Suite 2000 │ Seattle, Washingt[...]

Patient's name:

Your treatment

The treatment schedule below explains how the drugs for this treatment are given.

TC (docetaxel and cyclophosphamide)

This treatment cycle is repeated every 21 days. You will have 4 to 6 cycles.

Day	Treatment	How it is given	How long it takes
1	Docetaxel (dox-e-tax-elle)	By a drip into a vein	About 2.5 hours
	Cyclophosphamide (SYE-kloe-FOS-fa-mide)		
2	Pegfilgrastim (peg-fil-GRA-stim)	By injection under the skin	About 5 minutes

When to get help

Anticancer drugs (drugs used to treat cancer) can sometimes cause serious problems. It is important to get medical help immediately if you become unwell.

➕ **IMMEDIATELY go to your nearest hospital Emergency Department, or contact your doctor or nurse if you have any of the following at any time:**

Emergency contact details

Ask your doctor or nurse from your treating team who to contact if you have a problem.

Daytime:

Night/weekend:

Other instructions:

- a temperature of 38°C or higher
- chills, sweats, shivers or shakes
- shortness of breath
- uncontrolled vomiting or diarrhoea
- pain, tingling or discomfort in your chest or arms
- you become unwell.

During your treatment immediately tell the doctor or nurse looking after you if you get any of the following problems:

- leaking from the area where the drugs are being given
- pain, stinging, swelling or redness in the area where the drugs are being given or at any inject[...] site
- [...] rash[...]shortness of breath, wheez[...], feeling dizzy or unwell in any[...]c reaction).

Other information about your treatment

[...]change[...]you[...]or treatment rela[...]

OH IT'S ALSO THE DAY I'M DECLARED MENOPAUSAL

Just keep training

When in doubt keep training. The gym is always where I take refuge when everything else is chaos.

Back to Canberra & work

Setting up an innovation lab for my client in Canberra. It's a good distraction.

I'm one of those women who can perform at work in any situation, no matter what is going on. I can separate work from life and focus regardless.

I mention this to my client Paul and he uses a term I've never heard before but which I love – Work Athlete.

The idea that we've literally trained for decades to be Work Athletes and we can turn it on whenever we need to.

The "how are you?" question

When you have cancer this question becomes something you dread.

It's a standard greeting that everyone uses, and so you're faced with having to decide over and over through the course of a day what to say.

Your first thought....are they really interested and I tell them how I really am? Or is it just a pleasant greeting that's nothing more than a rhetorical question and we definitely should not get real?

It feels completely inauthentic to pretend that something this huge isn't happening so I usually say actually I have cancer and I have a lot going on but aside from that I'm great. Some people can handle this, but other times everything can get weird because they feel horribly uncomfortable and then you have to remove the discomfort for them.

Very often I'm bored of being a person with cancer. And so I just say good – which is true. In myself I am very good. Never happier. And there are plenty of other things I'd rather talk about.

Sometimes you say I'm excellent, and you really are. But they don't believe you can be excellent when you have cancer, because they know they wouldn't be, and they go on to repeatedly ask you are you sure, and you have to repeatedly assure them that actually I'm better than fine, I'm going to come through this like a fucking mofo, just watch me rise, and can we move on now.

Sometimes you tell people and they get really sad or even cry, which is not helpful. I've got enough to handle over here without worrying about how you're feeling.

Sometimes you tell people and then you ask them how they are – because it's polite to be reciprocal – and they say oh nothing compared to what you're going through. And then the conversation ends abruptly, because they feel they have nothing to say, and you leave feeling like you were a selfish conversationalist.

Sometimes you tell people and they are genuinely interested. You have lovely conversations with people, even with compete strangers – you swap stories, and between you there is this unique understanding of a very big life thing. It's a rare moment of deep human connection. I've actually made lots of lovely new friends in this process.

One time someone asked me how I was and went on to tell me about their friend who died.

Don't do this.

6   35   131

Shopping for the apocalypse

Not only is there no toilet paper, tissues, flour, pasta or rice, there is also a run on sardines.

So people are making some weird dish comprised of pasta and sardines?

With the lovely @lisarenkin

17   28   14

LOOKING BACK

My friend Lisa took me for breakfast and then shopping.

Over breakfast I showed her my list of things the chemo people tell you to buy to help with the cold cap, and the list of foods they recommend for nausea.

Most of it wasn't in the shops. Because of covid the shops are already running out of nearly everything. I'm smiling in the picture because that's what you do when someone takes a picture – but inside I was starting to feel really antsy and vulnerable.

I think I'm about to do chemo and there's no food in the shops. WTF am I going to do?

How will I eat? How will I shop?

I decide to do chemo today

So while everyone else has been panicking about covid, I've been sitting quietly with myself the last 2 weeks pondering whether or not I'm prepared to do the chemo that was recommended to me by my oncologist.

She doesn't like the look of my 10 year recurrence rate.

It's the shittiest decision ever – because there are no good options really.

Anyway after a week where I decided I'd be willing to die early rather than do it, I decided today to go ahead.

It starts Friday. I'm not exactly happy about it. But I've made my peace with it, and I'll do it the way I do everything – all in.

The fascinating thing is that my first question was whether or not I would lose my hair. It's not about the hair per se, it's about the brutalisation of my body. Anyway it's 50/50 on that one, so I've been enjoying having hair all week just in case.

Always onwards.

19   48   39

The chemo decision

This is for anyone who's borderline on whether chemo is recommended or who isn't sure they want to do it.

Deciding whether or not to do chemo is one of the hardest decisions I've ever had to make.

I really didn't want to do it – my body was screaming at me not to.

But my oncologist strongly recommended it: from her perspective I'm in a high-risk group for the cancer returning – 30% recurrence rate in 10 years.

And mine was already in the lymph nodes – only 1 lymph node in all the 20 that they took out, but that's enough to get an oncologist wanting to send you to the chemo ward instantly.

Sitting in a meeting talking about my chances of survival and possible early death is the most surreal thing I've ever experienced. You wonder if it's really happening and how did you get here. Especially when she lands the punch

"If you don't do chemo and it comes back in an organ it's automatically stage 4 and there's nothing we can do for you".

I tried to point out that I exercise regularly and eat well and meditate every day – but she retorted with "you already do all of those things and you still got cancer". I went in there with all my ideas about energy healing and diet, and came out scared and second-guessing myself.

It's always hard to know what to make of medical diagnoses.

You don't have enough knowledge to actually interrogate them properly, and you're having to make big decisions with not much time, very little energy if you've undergone surgery already, and a lot of heightened emotions. And medical language is such that the focus is on the risk of death rather than the chance of survival – it's how medicine works.

I negotiated 2 weeks to think about it. In retrospect this was a great thing to do, because I was much more at peace about my decision when I made it.

The first week after the meeting with the oncologist I was firm on not doing the chemo. I wanted to go down the energy healing route, and manage my health better with better food and less stress. I was sure I wasn't going to do it. Some women said I should get a second opinion, but I chose not to. How would I even begin to process competing medical opinions? I knew absolutely nothing about cancer, and making myself an expert would take time I didn't have.

I used the time to research alternative treatments – there's a lot in Mexico for instance, and Europe. I even searched for miracle cures in the Amazon. But I realised I was too tired to go anywhere else, and how would I know that the doctors in any of those places were better than the doctors I have? And then it was clear that the borders would be shutting soon anyway, as a result of covid, and going anywhere else simply wasn't an option.

I read a book that got me excited about immunotherapy and vitamin C as an alternative to chemo. The oncologist said immunotherapy wasn't suitable for my particular cancer, and she didn't recommend vitamin C. So that was the end of that.

The most useful thing I did was to speak to other people – some who had done chemo and others who hadn't.

I have a friend who said he bitterly regretted doing it. There were women who'd done chemo and who said it's the best thing they ever did. There were stories of those who had tried to manage it naturally and when it didn't work they turned to chemo by which time it was too late, and they died: I kept hearing "yeah, she passed". This was a huge reality check. I spoke to one of the lovely nurses who has been with me throughout this process who said she had never met a woman who hadn't made the choice that was right for her, even the women who had refused and had gone on to die.

After really listening to the ones who'd chosen not to do chemo, this is what I heard: You have to be rock solid on diet, you have to completely de-stress your life, and you have to be prepared to heal any underlying emotional or spiritual issues that are causing dis-ease in your body. It takes complete dedication – you're managing your cancer forever essentially. You have to have the gift of money and time for alternative treatments and an intense food regime: alternative treatments often aren't available on the public health system and so you have to research and find them, and you have to pay for them yourself. And you need to be able to sift the practitioners who are genuine from those who are unscrupulous people making money from your desperation.

In the end the non-chemo route looked like really hard work with an unknown end point.

I decided I didn't want to be a hostage to this thing forever, I don't want it to define me.

The oncologist had filled my mind with a mental image of microscopic cancer cells circulating my body just looking for a place to grow a brand new tumour that would surely kill me. I think if you walk away from chemo you have to do it without a single shred of doubt – doubt leaves room for the cancer to come back.

And so I chose the chemo. I decided to suck it up so that I could get on with my life more quickly. I did what was in front of me, that's all any of us can ever do. This was my best option. There are often no great options in cancer, and no right or wrong answers, just whatever is right for you.

We all have different belief systems and different attitudes towards risk – the risk of dying on the one hand, the risk of chemo side-effects on the other.

We all have a different ability to do the other things you would need to do if you are going to walk away from it constraints of time and money.

How I made my decision:

I allowed myself to really feel into the idea that there is a choice here, as horrible as it is, and that I can choose to say no if I want to.

I allowed myself some time to cry some tears, to rage at the medical system, to have a tantrum, to try out how it felt to say no, I refuse to do this thing. I allowed all my feelings, without getting stuck in them or judging them, until eventually the noise cleared, and there was peace.

Then there was a day it felt right to say yes, and it felt right in my body. I realised this meant that I had to surrender to it fully, or it cannot do it's work.

The thing is to not look back. The decision is made. It's done.

My experience was that there were those who didn't understand why I would even debate doing the chemo – they would quote me facts and tell me what they thought I should do. There were others who thought I should be more 'positive' when I explained why the whole idea made me angry and filled me with dread.

Many of them had never had cancer or had to put their bodies through chemo. It was exhausting having to explain to people that I've got this.

I'm making a big decision, and I'm scared and confused, but I've got this.

Breast cancer as an initiation

I got a beautiful email from a Facebook friend who I have never met the day before my first treatment:

"It indeed is not an initiation for the feeble minded, so hurray for your courage, it is an eye of the needle opportunity, and when walked through consciously miracles abound, actual angels accompany you, your ancestors applaud and cheer you on, the masters walk all the way up to the portal with you and a new dawn awaits at the other end. Trust those who you energetically feel have come to help you ease through and don't waste energy on convincing anyone of what they cannot understand at this point... inspire yourself to become the inspiration... stand strong, be focussed with soft eyes and piercing gentle unwinking gaze... make self care a priority."

This becomes a thing I go back to over and over. It reminds me what I'm doing when I lose faith. Thank you Ori Ana, the friend I've never met.

I can see in the dark

LOOKING BACK

My bestie from the UK was meant to be coming to stay for a while to help me do chemo.

I had a story about the chemo – that it was all going to be ok because I wouldn't be alone. He would be with me. We might even have some fun in the in-between times. He's been my bestie for decades and I haven't seen him for a couple of years.

I made a lovely bedroom up for him. I sent him this picture. I was excited. (Looking at it now it drives me nuts that I didn't bother to straighten out the doona underneath.)

On the 10th of March there had been a press conference where it became clear that covid is serious and we all knew a lockdown was coming in Melbourne.

This was that crazy week when you could feel the world contracting – the news was full of borders closing and flights being cancelled. It was chaos. My friend was still trying to make it, but his options were narrowing by the day.

The penny started dropping. My friend wasn't coming. I was going to be doing chemo, and living alone, in a lockdown that any one of us could see was going to run for a long time.

This thing that scared me so much – chemo – I was going to do on my own. Completely on my own. A single person who lives alone, and also an expat who's a long way from friends and family, in a lockdown kind of alone.

When he said he wasn't coming I sat in my kitchen for hours that evening thinking holy fuck how did I get here: How did I get cancer? How did I get to be doing it alone in a country I don't call home, and in the middle of a pandemic that kills people with cancer? It was the most surreal moment of my life.

I remember turning off the light that night to go to bed and feeling a rising panic verging on terror as the house went dark. Turning the lights off felt really symbolic.

I can't do this. I can't do this. I can't do this.

But as I stood there in the pitch black another voice said – oh but you can.

And I remember thinking to myself IT'S OK, I CAN SEE IN THE DARK. We do our spiritual practice for times like these.

I decided it was going to be ok. And the fear went, it just went. This is going to be hard, but I can do this. It's on.

Chemo 1: It's game time

Ok chemo is happening today. Friday the 13th of March. A friend Carmen who knows how much I'm struggling with it sends me this little mantra which I love:

> "EVERY HAND THAT TOUCHES ME IS A HEALING HAND, EVERY REMEDY THAT IS GIVEN TO ME IS A HEALING REMEDY".

I write it down so I can remind myself. I agreed to this. They're trying to help me. I have a gang – well 2 people. Delta and Graham.

First Delta and I go and get cake from the cafe on the ground floor of the hospital.

Arriving at reception I was surprised to be offered a choice of drinks and sandwiches. I don't know what I thought was going to happen today, but I didn't expect to eat. I had no idea that you don't feel awful while it's happening because they pump you full of steroids. I actually felt fucking fantastic once I settled into what was happening.

I had no idea how peaceful it would be in there either, people just getting on with it, no fuss, no drama. I think we might have been a bit rowdy relatively speaking, it was my way of coping – not sure if we were annoying or entertaining to the other patients.

My blog post for the day was 'It was a breeze. I travelled to the place beyond reason and decided it would be so. Plus I got a lot of love from people.'

The place beyond reason – I had never used this phrase before but today it just felt right. My instinct was that this was not a time for thinking about things but a time to tune into something else. I had no words yet for what that meant but it settled me. I felt other–worldly, serene.

Cold cap

This ridiculous-looking hat is the cold cap treatment which gives you some chance of keeping your hair. I wanted to keep my hair so I signed up for it.

It's freezing but not particularly painful. It looked ridiculous – gave me chubby hamster cheeks.

I gave up after 1 treatment. My hair was falling out in massive chunks already – there was zero chance of saving it.

And we were right in the middle of the Melbourne covid situation. I didn't want to be in a hospital for one more minute than I needed to, and the cold cap added another hour on to my hospital trip.

The day after

Obviously the anti-nausea meds they give you in hospital are really good. Because I felt awesome yesterday and today I woke up with whole body pulsing, waves of nausea, and heat.

Managed to get some anti-nausea meds and my steroids down and then I went and lay on the bathroom floor tiles because they're lovely and cold.

In the end I had to creep In and wake up my friend @m_i_s_s_d_e_l_t_a who's staying with me and say I don't feel very well mum...

My mouth feels like cardboard. The bicarb mouth gargles are hideous. My porridge that I normally love tasted like metal.

But I'm still cheerful, all the angels are with me, and I'm practising wigs just in case.

28   23   32

Off to training

The oncologist says that exercise helps the chemo to do its job. Plus I'm on steroids (the day after chemo) and they feel fabulous in spite of the nausea.

So I take my nausea meds, ride the steroids and off to training.

They were damn good squats.

State of emergency

STATE OF EMERGENCY
ANNOUNCED.

LOCKDOWN IS COMING
FOR SURE.

IT'S BEEN COMING
FOR AGES.

THE TENSION IN MELBOURNE
IS EXCRUCIATING.

The borders are closed

The day the borders closed and the flights stopped and I had a creeping realisation that this place here, a place I have adopted but which is not home, and where I don't have many people, is where I am for the indefinite future.

I am here, with cancer, in the middle of a pandemic, with no guaranteed work, and living on my own, with no way to get home.

I wake up at 3am the next day gasping for air and crying. Claustrophobia and panic.

Pam and Therese in New York City happened to be up (the benefit of time zones) and we do a video chat, which makes everything alright.

27 MARCH 2020

Cancer patients in Melbourne die of covid

Melbourne's first covid casualties have just been recorded.

Cancer patients. In a cancer ward.

I'm over 50 and I have cancer – does that mean the virus is more likely to get me?

And if the hospitals are over-run does that mean I'm less likely to get a ventilator?

Am I going to die of covid because I have cancer?

I can't believe I'm even thinking about this. It's nuts.

It's only hair

Was having a good hair day today, but out of nowhere my whole scalp was itchy as hell and sort of throbbing – it felt as if every follicle in my head was on fire. A lot of it fell out in the shower. And now it's all over the house. Even though I did the cold cap treatment there's zero chance that my hair is making it all the way. So I guess that's happening. Currently eating chocolate in bed.

I had wanted a lesbian chic quiff for a few weeks before going bald but it wasn't to be. The hair came out in a clump from the top, so there weren't many options.

As I was standing in the shower with handfuls of the stuff I started to cry because that's what you do when your hair falls out during chemo. It took about 30 seconds for me to realise that the chemo hair story wasn't my story, it belongs to someone else, and that while it's a bit sad to lose it I don't actually care. In fact I can choose not to care. And so I did.

And that is the end of the story.

38   36   42

Today's mood

Had all sorts of mood today. Decided to capture it.

Maybe because the hair is coming off in a few days.

2 APRIL 2020
GI Jane – the day the hair came off

There was no point fighting it, it was all coming out. Felt sad for a few minutes, but I've decided not to get lost in this. I can't.

What I heard a lot from people is the comment "you have a lovely shaped head".

My instinct was to keep touching my head. I've never felt it before.

120   61   65

LOOKING BACK

What I didn't write in my original blog is that my hair coming out was actually an ecstatic event. The moment in the shower that I realised I had the power to care or not care was a moment of pure power, a total rush.

One of the biggest moments of the year for me. And probably my life.

I knew intellectually that you had the power to decide the story you're telling yourself in any moment, but I'd never needed to do it under pressure, when it really mattered.

Being able to do this for myself felt so freaking amazing. I realised I'm the master of my own life. I get to choose the story of my life.

I noticed that someone implicitly criticised me in their comment on my post. I really remember that. I think they might have felt I was criticising others who do care about their hair?

It was the first time I noticed that not everyone is going to vibe with my way of dealing with this. It was really important to me to not be a victim to the cancer. That's why I chose to shave it off rather than sit and hope that I might be able to keep it. It was a modicum of control in a situation that was very much out of my control.

And choosing my story also made me not a victim. Cancer is huge and it can eat you up, it can become everything. I didn't want this for myself.

The cancer is happening, the hair is coming out. But it's not all of me, it's not my whole story, it's just a thing that's happening right now.

Chemo 2

Chemo round 2. And it's covid time. Hazmat suit inspired by Naomi Campbell – google hazmat suit if you don't know what I mean.

My friend Graham drives me to the hospital, but he's not allowed in. We have no idea at this point whether this covid is serious or not so I go all-out with the PPE just in case – it feels that there's more covid in the hospitals than anywhere. I'm a bit less fazed now, and am able to look around me. I can see some very very sick and frail people.

I felt like a bit of a fraud making so much drama out of my cancer. I particularly remember a very old man who looked emaciated, and his wife who was sitting beside him looking so scared. If I'm finding this hard, how hard must it be when you're older and your body is more frail? It was one of those moments where I realised how lucky I am, cancer or not.

My mantra for this chemo, the thing I would whisper to myself when I felt that I was losing my courage:

JUST KEEP SAYING YES – LOVE IT LIKE YOU CHOSE IT.

How your mind plays tricks on you

Something I wrote during chemo today: How your mind plays tricks with you.

When I got #breastcancer I thought it was the worst thing in the world to happen to me. I was gutted. I got over that pretty quickly though.

And then I thought that having #chemotherapy was the worst thing ever. But I got over that pretty quickly too.

And then I thought that I could deal with having #chemo but I couldn't deal with losing my hair. I lost it yesterday. I already love my new look. Who doesn't want to be told they look like Sigourney Weaver in Alien?

And then along came covid and suddenly having cancer and catching the virus was the worst thing that could happen.

And then, once you realise that most of us aren't going to die of the virus, the idea of having cancer and not having a job and being broke for the rest of this year was going to be the worst thing.

And then I stopped thinking that any of it was bad. It was exhausting.
It's just a way for your mind to play tricks with you. It wants something to do. It wants you to be fearful. I decided

to just live with what came every day. I remembered we can all bear more than we realise.

Right now I have a lot to bear, but I can. And I'll get stronger as I do. It's life training.

Instead of focusing on judgements about what's happening I'm focussed on whatever is going to come out the other side of this. How I'll be different, bigger, more. My mantra has become 'eat it up and turn it into gold'.

I also sat with death for a while. I think that most of our fear in life can be traced back to fear of death.

And I thought that while I don't really want to die yet, it doesn't scare me, and so most of these other things that happen along the way shouldn't either.

My teacher always says 'nothing matters' and it doesn't really. It's not nihilistic, it's liberating. It's not 'not caring' – it's not giving power to things so they don't have power over you. It's freedom.

14   15   15

Home from chemo
– that steroid glow

The day after

Steroid comedown and in bed feeling gruesome

I made the rookie error after the first chemo of not eating. I lost several kilos in weight and it made me feel worse. On this chemo I realised I was going to have to let go of all my healthy eating ideas and just get calories in – whatever I could stomach. I gave in to whatever my body asked for – ice cream, cans of coke, cheesy beans on toast, croissants with butter and jam – things I never normally eat. My body didn't want broccoli and spinach and all the healthy things I do usually eat. I knew I was through the worst when I craved real food again.

LOOKING BACK

I wish I'd taken more of these pictures. They speak for themselves. I was so busy trying to stay positive, to not collapse – for good reasons – that I forgot to document the reality, the challenge in it.

I find it hard to look at these – I hear a voice that says 'you look ugly'. It's such a weird response – utterly ridiculous. It shows how deep the programming goes around women and their looks.

Even though I was documenting/ blogging my experience I didn't dare put any of these on social media. Not just because of the ugly factor, although it was that, but also I didn't want pity. There's a culture on social media where people use it to elicit sympathy, and I didn't want sympathy.

The challenging thing with chemo – for me anyway – is that it felt like an all-over central nervous system pain – it's poisoning I suppose. It's holding in vomit, not being able to see well. It's feeling really vulnerable, especially living on your own and when no-one is allowed into the house. I can't do much for myself – or my dogs. I don't like feeling that vulnerable at all.

The discomfort of the nausea was really challenging to me. Even with years of mindfulness practice I find it hard to separate myself from this sick feeling. I KNOW it's temporary, that it will pass, and that I'll smile again, but right now it feels interminable and I feel like a small child. When I was a kid being sick was the worst thing that could happen to me. I remember I used to cry every time I was sick, it's always been a trigger for self-pity.

It occurs to me that we humans can bear an existential crisis (am I going to die?) so long as we're not in pain or suffering on a minute by minute basis.

12 APRIL 2020

I'm in The Age

The Age is a Melbourne newspaper. They wanted stories of people at home alone in lockdown.

Love the awesome photo of the house - he flew a drone over.

The interview was done over the fence because no-one is allowed in the house now.

https://www.theage.com.au/
national/victoria/life-in-
isolation-portraits-of-a-
society-in-lockdown-
20200402-p54gei. html

Maggie & me

Me and Maggie, doing what we do every evening these days – eating too much. This is her saying 'If I look at you like I love you, you'll give me food yeah?'

Little Morgaine goes off straight to bed every night after our walk. Maggie stays up with me. I think she loves me. But also she knows she can work me for treats. Just her and me together in the kitchen.

Most nights of the lockdown it would be just me and Maggie alone together in the house. Some music, some food, maybe zoom to a friend. We became evening eating buddies. She likes crisps, I like crisps. Basically we get lockdown fat together.

Death & dying

One of the upsides of lockdown is that lots of organisations have put their content online. This is me and Morgaine watching a seminar from the US on shamanism and conscious dying. I've become really interested in death.

A friend Ashley called last night. We haven't spoken in years but he saw a Facebook post and reached out. He's the only person who went straight to it: "do you mind me asking how you feel about dying?".

It was such a relief for someone to ask me as if it was the most normal thing in the world.

(Even now, more than a year later, he was still the only person who asked me the question directly.)

I've never thought about my own death before and I've been noticing my reaction to the idea of it. I realised I was comforting myself with "it's ok, my soul is eternal". I have no idea where this thought came from. I've never had this conversation with myself before.

Is this what the mind does to comfort itself, to avoid the idea of its own dissolution? Pacifies us with the idea of eternal life?

Or do I believe this?

Deadlifts

Final training session for this 9 week block where I've worked up from a few tentative post-surgery reps @ 40KG to 50 reps @ 90KG.

Did 3 sets of 10 @ 90KG and then, because I was running short on time, I decided to merge 2 sets into 1 and do a final set of 20 reps @ 90KG. It wasn't easy.

I can feel fatigue from the chemo in my muscles now.

Anyway will rest next week and after that see if there's enough in my body to go up to 100KG, which would put me back into the work zone.

14   15   15

24 APRIL 2020

Chemo 3

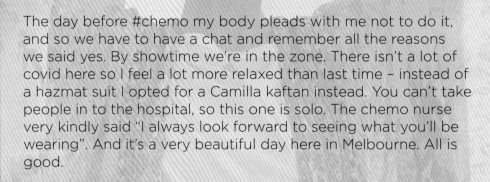

The day before #chemo my body pleads with me not to do it, and so we have to have a chat and remember all the reasons we said yes. By showtime we're in the zone. There isn't a lot of covid here so I feel a lot more relaxed than last time – instead of a hazmat suit I opted for a Camilla kaftan instead. You can't take people in to the hospital, so this one is solo. The chemo nurse very kindly said "I always look forward to seeing what you'll be wearing". And it's a very beautiful day here in Melbourne. All is good.

63   45   39

My mantra for this chemo

MORE LOVE MORE LOVE MORE LOVE.

I repeat this to myself over and over.
It calms my central nervous system instantly.
I just whisper it to myself, in the most gentle way, and I come
right back to the most beautiful softness, loving myself,
loving my body.

Back from the hospital – I stop dancing

I'd been kitchen dancing myself happy the last little while. And usually I would have a dance at home the night I got home from chemo - house music, R&B, poppy stuff – partly steroid happy, partly relieved to have survived another round. But this was the night I stopped. I couldn't feel a beat in my body any more, everything felt heavy. This was the day I started to lose myself a bit – my connection to my body, my essence, my vitality. The treatment was starting to overcome me.

Instead I listened to some opera – Jessye Norman. It suited my mood better and calms my nervous system. I started listening to classical music from now on.

The day after chemo feeling gruesome

Looking at this photo makes me flinch. But this is the reality of chemo no matter how positive you are and how good your mindset it. So there it is.

The dogs love my bed weeks. Me not so much. I can't read or watch TV, I can't concentrate. I spend a lot of time doing social media, emailing people, just to stay connected - it's lockdown so no-one can come over to keep me company. But most of it is just lying there feeling sick, wondering whether it's time to take the next anti-nausea meds, wondering what will happen if you take them early, lying on the bathroom floor because the tiles are cool. Dragging myself out of bed to walk the dogs.

I would be lost without my ladies.

Worst birthday ever

Home alone because of lockdown. No hair. Pissing down with rain. Can't drink because of the cancer/chemo. I tried to make a day of it – I got dressed up and did make-up. I'm not a birthday person at all, but today the loneliness hurts like hell. I ended up falling into a depressed state and going to bed early. Didn't speak to anyone on the phone or answer anyone on social media. Just needed the day over and done with.

30 reps at 100KG

Went up to 100KG this week –
the first time back in the real
work zone since surgery.

Managed 3 sets of 10, which
would normally be easy, but it
wasn't, my body is just slow and
heavy after the chemo last week.

My legs ache all the time. I don't
really like how rounded my back
looks here, but I'll fix that when
I'm less fatigued.

Still moving forwards bit by bit.

19   33   14

Reggie!

My dear friend Henry's dad Reggie – who I've never met – has me at the top of his list of daily prayers apparently. I'm not religious at all, but I'm extremely grateful. He sends me a book by Jonathan Sacks, the British Jewish Rabbi.

My favourite bit, which I go back to all the time is this: "...when we open ourselves to the universe we find God reaching out to us. At that moment we make the life-changing discovery that, although we are utterly insignificant, we are also utterly significant, a fragment of God's presence in the world... we know that this day, this moment, this place, this circumstance, is full of the light of infinite radiance... if we make ourselves transparent to existence, then our lives too radiate that Divine presence...."

I love the idea that when we reach out to the universe we find it reaching back to us. That we're at once totally insignificant and utterly significant. Henry and I talk a lot – he explains emunah to me, the Jewish idea of a faith beyond reason.

It seems counter-intuitive but to me it feels easier to access this faith in times of distress. I think it's only when we're backed into a corner that we're prepared to believe that we have greater powers than we know, and that there is magic in the universe beyond what we can see.

Reggie and Henry are writing a book together called *The Stories I Told My Son*. Details here: https://www.facebook.com/thestoriesitoldmyson/

Being bald

I read an article by an oncologist who said that in her experience the 'will I lose my hair?' question is often the last thing that people ask. For me it was the first. Which is interesting because I've never really thought of myself as vain. I'm more of a tomboy than a girly girl. I hardly wear make-up, I don't even own a brush or comb and never use a hairdryer, and I spend most of my time in dog clothes or sportswear. Plus I've always thought of myself as a feminist – more concerned with my brain and my personality than my looks. Losing my hair showed me I'm a lot more vain than I cared to admit, and turned out to be a fascinating exploration of my sense of self.

When I went for the hair shave I initially left some on because I wasn't ready to be completely bald. But it looked patchy and strange so a week later I took the rest off. I did it myself, which felt important. I wish I'd done the big one myself.

I realised that I was doing things to pretty myself up – head wraps, make-up, earrings – and while it's totally ok to want to be pretty, actually all of this was avoidance – not accepting the reality of what was happening to me, and being ok with it. I couldn't look at myself in the mirror and when I did there was a voice that said God you look ugly.

I was worried about what other people were thinking. When I noticed people – men – staring at me in the street I was aware that I was worried whether or not they would find me attractive, which is a strange thought to have when you're dealing with cancer, a thing that can kill you and that is way more important than whether some random guy on the street thinks I'm hot or not. The archetypal idea that long hair on a woman is attractive goes deep. (Aside – I actually had a LOT of positive comments from men about the short hair – the references tend to be Linda Hamilton, Demi Moore, and Sigourney Weaver, so there's clearly men who vibe with this look very much indeed.)

So I had a week where I took all those things away and made myself look at me entirely unadorned. And I started going into the world without the head wrap and getting used to the uncomfortable feeling that other people might be looking at me with either pity or horror. I see now why nuns and committed Buddhists shave their hair. It's a removal of a layer of human pretence and artifice.

I haven't really wanted to do the wig thing. I understand entirely why a woman would choose to go down that road, but I wanted to eyeball this thing directly, to not flinch, and to see what there was for me to learn. It was a deep practice in saying yes to life, to loving myself and loving my body, no matter what. Looking in the mirror and seeing yourself not just totally bald, but looking haggard and frail, and with skin that's almost grey is quite a trip. I just kept saying over and over to myself and my body I love you, you're doing a great job, keep going.

It wasn't just vanity though, I was concerned about what people at work would think – would they think less of my ability to do my job because I had cancer... At first I wouldn't do it. I was happy to talk about having cancer, I wasn't embarrassed by that, but being bald is a very visual reminder that you do have cancer, and I didn't want them thinking that because of my cancer I couldn't perform. In the end I decided to just own it. I'm good at my job,

really good, and that's all there is to say on that. And in the end I just wanted to be real. This photo is the first day I went to work bald. I love the vibe: I look like I'm in a ska band in the UK in the late seventies.

There was also something else I didn't expect: I noticed that I felt different in my human interactions without hair. There's nothing to hide behind. I felt that all my thoughts and feelings were fully on show – I felt I had to work harder. I also noticed myself thinking that I should smile more to avoid looking too tough and off-putting without the hair to soften my face. Which is another dilemma for women because if we're not smiling people think we look bitchy.

There were still days/weeks that I hated it. On one of my down weeks my bestie Matt said I looked like a Hot Alien he'd seen in a film once. So that was my reframe when I struggled: I'm a Hot Alien. It's invaluable to have gay friends who tell you you look hot even on your worst days.

I don't know why I didn't realise this but it isn't just head hair. I had no hair left anywhere on my body. I loved the smooth legs, they felt quite lovely, but I disliked the no pubes thing very much. It's not a look I've ever gone for. I thought I would find losing my eyelashes really hard – turns out I didn't even notice I'd lost them until one day I went to put mascara on and there wasn't much to put mascara on. Like so many things, real life is often not as bad as your imagination tells you it will be.

Turbans at work

If I say so myself I totally killed my work look with turbans.

I had never tried a turban before, but they became my go-to. They look fantastic – they really finish a look off. You can make them look really really smart.

I got to the point where any bit of material around the house was being turned into a headwrap. If you're a working woman or you need to be able to dress formally don't fear the turban.

15 MAY 2020
Chemo 4

LAST CHEMO TODAY. And I felt like being a dragon, so out came the dragon kimono.

Having #breastcancer and doing #chemo started off as this big emotional thing, particularly when the virus appeared to be rampant and there was this idea that it was killing people with cancer. I've spent the best part of 6 weeks at home, mostly alone and without the touch of another person, barely leaving the house, pondering my own death, and wondering if it was my time to go.

But as I meditated on it, it very quickly became no-thing. It's just another part of being alive, and it only has power over you if you allow it. You can still wake up every day and love life and fill your world with light. We're all gonna die and that's ok.

Every time I do chemo I re-read the message from Ori: "it is not an initiation for the feeble minded, so hurray for your courage, it is an eye of the needle opportunity, and when walked through consciously miracles abound, actual angels accompany you, your ancestors applaud and cheer you on, the masters walk all the way up to the portal with you and a new dawn awaits at the other end". I've walked through the portal.

This experience has already changed me and I'm glad for it, despite everything. And I'm ready to move on. It's done. What's next?

33   19   14

122

Why don't I feel elated?

I come home after the final round of chemo – my friend Graham drops me off because still no-one is allowed in your home.

I expect to feel elated.

Instead I lie on the floor and sob for hours.

I haven't cried properly before now. I've had tears.

But I haven't allowed one of those 'this is so fucking hard and I feel sorry for myself' moments where you put aside being brave for a little while and you sob and sob until you're exhausted and your face is swollen, but it feels kind of good to have it out your system.

I've been holding on for dear life. You can't cry when you're hanging on that tight.

It feels that I'm through the worst, although I'm rapidly learning that cancer is one of those things where you never know where the end is, or even if there is an end.

There seems to always be something worse just over the horizon.

In bed for almost a week

As each chemo goes on I have to spend longer in bed recovering. This final one was a good 5 days in bed and a week before I felt good again. Cumulative poisoning.

Still in lockdown. No visitors.

But lots of people leaving food on the doorstep, without which I wouldn't be eating at all.

Maggie didn't leave my side all week.

A beautiful sunny day to get out of bed

After the chemo is done

The weeks after final chemo were brutal.

For a couple of days afterwards it was as if I'd been on a week-long bender – there's an unspecific pain, everywhere, and you have to just lie in bed and wait. I'm always struck by how much it shows on my face and in my eyes.

My legs in particular ache like hell, which makes powerlifting hard, and this week my fingernails have been throbbing too, they're turning brittle and white and peeling off. Eyelashes are mostly gone.

I go from too hot to freezing a hundred times a day, it's annoying how often I have to put clothes on and take them off again.

The nausea has been far worse than the other 3 rounds, but I've finally given in to just taking as many anti-nausea pills as I need and not even trying to be a trooper – just give me the meds.

I've worked so hard to accept the chemo into my body as medicine, but it's gruesome, and I'm glad it's over.

At the same time my mind is sharp, I feel really creative, and I have an exquisite sense of clarity and simplicity. The kind we only get when we've been forcibly stripped back, and are reminded that so much of life is just noise and how few things actually matter. I can't wait to put this knowing to use somehow. I promise myself to never forget.

Hilariously, it was only last night I had the realisation of how ill I've been and that cancer is quite serious. I was so busy just dealing with whatever was in front of me there wasn't room for that before.

I feel a door shut on an old version of me, and how much living there is still to do.

19   33   14

NOTE:
After this I don't do another social media post for almost 7 weeks. I was done, absolutely nothing to say.

The end of this phase

LOOKING BACK

This is my Tracey Emin style bed picture taken the day I got out of bed after my last round of chemo. It felt like the end of a massive phase.
It was hard: chemo, lockdown, winter.
I felt the presence of darkness.
I'm not sure if it was real or if the chemo drugs were playing havoc with my central nervous system.

The first chemo was relatively easy, but each subsequent one got harder – the fatigue, how it rips through your body. No matter how hard I worked to accept it I deeply resented having to have chemo at all – it felt like medicine from the Dark Ages. We still can't do better than this to cure cancer? I could have made it easier for myself if I'd resisted less. Sometimes there's a time to take the medicine and be grateful.

I lost a very significant relationship in this phase – probably the most important relationship in my life – and I wasn't sure if it was me or them. My emotions were all over the place. I may never know.

The house was a pigsty – because of lockdown the cleaner couldn't come and I was too tired to do anything.

The chemo had wrecked my diet – I used to eat well, and for months I'd been living on ice-cream, pasta, cans of coke, just to get calories in. That much sugar isn't good for your mental health or your body.

My concentration and memory were destroyed. I couldn't read, couldn't bear to watch TV, too much to process. I stared into space a lot, scrolled social media, because it's easy.

The loss of hair put my temperature control completely out of whack – too cold or too hot all the time. It was a constant low-level irritation, and it ruined my sleep, which in turn made me grumpy.

I don't remember much about the day to day detail, I've blocked it out. The prevailing memory is feeling sick, poisoned, fragile, vulnerable. And very heightened emotions. So much emotion. I was realising that cancer isn't what I thought it was: that I wasn't going to be bouncing back as quickly as I had thought, and that actually cancer was kicking my arse.

There were many times I felt I had failed. I thought that after years of doing spiritual work I should be able to glide through all this like it ain't no thing. I had failed the grand test and that was it. These ideas would get under my skin for a while and then I would come back to asking myself "did you do your best?" and the answer was yes. This situation is hard. I'm doing cancer and living alone in the most surreal of situations. Yes I did my best. So just keep going Jane I would say to myself. Just keep going.

The Paradox

I had the feeling that I'd never been so vulnerable and so strong at the same time

This was the lowest point in many ways. But because of that it was also the most powerful. To survive it, I had to become someone and something else. What I didn't see at the time is that I wasn't completely lost. There was fear but there was also strength. And at the same time as doubting everything I was also in command of myself in ways in which I didn't really understand. All I knew at the time was that I had the distinct feeling of leaving a version of me behind.

Covid & lockdown

I WROTE THIS DIARY NOTE BECAUSE IN LATER YEARS I WANT TO REMEMBER HOW WEIRD IT WAS AND WHAT WE SURVIVED.

I remember...

Wondering seriously if this was my time to go – the news full of cancer patients not getting their treatment and dying, or covid patients with cancer being refused treatment and I seriously thought my time might be up. Having to be ok with that if that's what happens.

Supermarkets with hardly anything in and no online delivery and my being too nervous to go in them because my immune system was so compromised. Wondering if the whole food chain was about to break down. Panic-buying 6 months of dog food, coffee, and protein powder while everyone else seemed more interested in toilet roll.

The nurses at chemo not wearing PPE, while I was covered head to toe. Going home and saying to friends 'I can't believe they didn't have PPE in the chemo ward'. On a later visit I asked them why and they said they had decided not to because there wasn't enough and they wanted to make sure their colleagues dealing with covid had equipment. And thinking wow you're so much braver than I would be.

The day I had had a sinus infection for almost 2 weeks, it just wouldn't go away, and I could hardly breathe and I convinced myself I had THE VIRUS and I had a panic attack and had to ask a friend to come over and sit with me. Of course I was fine as soon as she was there and I took a valium.

Sitting alone in my house for months. Not having another person touch me or even allowing them to get close just in case.

Noticing my friends around me have nightmares and anxiety. Feeling the pain of so many others in the world who were losing everything.

Initially spending a lot of time trying to work out what the hell was happening here before giving up needing to know and just accepting that it just is and all I can do is deal with whatever is in front of me.

Asking the divine for help

Before all of this I would have called myself a spiritual person. Right now though everything feels so hard I'm doubting what I thought I believed.

You read things like 'the universe has got your back' and you think has it? Has it really? Because it sure doesn't feel like it right now. A lot of spiritual catchphrases just sound like complete claptrap to me in this place I'm at.

The love and light phrase that gets used so much really irritates me. It's easy to feel love and light when things are going 'well'. It's so much harder when things aren't going the way you want them to. And then I think, well that's my work then: to be able to feel love when all these things are going on. It must be possible.

I wonder if I've done something 'wrong' spiritually, and that this is why I got ill.

I was completely terrified that I was failing so badly at being spiritual in this cancer journey that I would be plunged into darkness and never come out. I start to think I don't know how to do this – how to have cancer and to keep believing in life.

I'm at the point where I'm realising that this is harder than I thought it was going to be and my old ways aren't going to cut it. I need to go to a deeper level. And then one day I start what I can only describe as praying, although I'm not sure that's what it is. I've never done this before, but I'm running on instinct. I think it's the first time I've ever asked the universe for help. I have a mantra I use every day, in the shower. I stand under the warm running water and say the same thing over and over, every single day for months.

MAY I BE STRONG. MAY I KNOW GRACE. MAY I BE LOVE. MAY I LET GO OF ALL THAT IS NOT GOD.

I don't know who or what I'm praying to. I know it's not to an off-planet God, that's not my thing.

I'm not praying to be saved from death, I'm not bargaining or negotiating. I'm praying for the courage to be able to say yes to what life is giving me. I'm looking for the strength to keep going, and to not fall into despair.

It was only looking back that I realised what I was doing: I was reaching into the deepest part of myself and invoking a higher consciousness that I was going to need to make it through this. I was literally breathing life into a version of me that was so much bigger than I'd ever been before. And I was asking the divine for help. A lot of help. I felt I couldn't do this on my own.

I feel and see a violet light with me at all times. I'm not alone.

Weed

I start using weed to get me through chemo – it helped with appetite, sleep, but also my overall mood. Honestly I would have been lost without it. I'm ok about using props when you need them.

I hate tobacco, so I would smoke a neat weed joint in the evenings, snuggled up in bed with the dogs, and some comedy.

I rewatched every episode of Arrested Development and Schitt's Creek. I would look forward to my evenings – everything was so serious at this time, and it was time to just check out and have a giggle.

Quietly, LOTS of people shared with me that their mum/dad/ sister had had cancer and that they had used weed to deal with the effects of the chemo, and to help ease their way towards the end of life. As far as I'm concerned this should be offered to anyone with cancer who wants it.

If you don't like smoking it, there's CBD oil, and there's edibles – you can make all sorts of things to eat with it.

TIPS FOR
Chemotherapy

 For nausea: Buy mints, make fresh mint or ginger tea.

 If you have mouth ulcers try gargling water, salt, and baking soda: 1/4 teaspoon baking soda, 1/8 teaspoon salt, 1 cup of warm water.

 Line up things to watch that are easy on the brain and the central nervous system: comedies for instance and podcasts that you can listen to without having to have your eyes open.

 Try your best to eat healthy food during chemo – but if you can't face fruit and veggies, even low nutrition food is better than eating nothing and losing lots of weight. Smoothies (fruit, healthy fat, and protein powder) and soups are a great way to get nutrients in when you can't bear to eat solids.

 Buy a blender if you don't have one.

 If you have a freezer put food that you like to eat in there ahead of time.

 If you have dogs, make sure to avoid dog poo. And protect your dog from you by making sure they don't eat any of your vomit.

 Drink prune juice or take Senna tablets at night to avoid constipation from the anti-nausea meds. Constipation on top of chemo side-effects is very demoralising.

 If you're likely to have to say goodbye to your hair buy some nice hats, and learn to make turbans with head scarfs – it's very cold without hair. Consider being proactive and just taking it off rather than waiting and hoping – it might feel more empowering.

 Make some video of the occasion, get some lovely photos taken – you will look beautiful and fierce, and they're great to look back on: you see how far you've come.

 Once your hair is growing back keep shaving and shaving until it's strong enough to grow.

 If you have pins and needles in the body (neuropathy): Most of these go away after treatment, although it takes time.

 Ask your surgeon/oncologist about using supplements such as vitamin C, medicinal mushrooms, CBD oil, smoking or eating weed, to ease the symptoms and to support your immune system. It's always best to check before taking things.

 Keep moving as much as you can. There's tons of research which shows it helps your body recover from cancer and it makes you feel better. Even walks and stretching are good if that's all you've got.

I start radio

I start radio on the 9th of June.

They give you a couple of weeks to recover after your last chemo, before it's on with the next thing.

It was every single day for 3 weeks initially. They added another week on just as I was about to do my last day, so it ended up being 4 weeks. Another one of those cancer trapdoors. I was gutted. I was exhausted and so ready to be done. I cried.

I did tons of journaling, but I didn't take many photos of this phase and I didn't do a single blog post between the 21st of May and the 13th of July. I had nothing to say to the world.

I was a whole other level of exhausted.

The radiologist said the fatigue is the result of the work the body is having to do: the radio kills the cells around the site of the cancer, so the body has to process all that cell death, and at the same time it stimulates the body to process new cells. It all requires a lot of energy. I noticed my appetite went through the roof in this phase: I ate and ate and ate. Didn't put any weight or body fat on, so my body must have been using it all.

To be able to keep working I was getting up at 4am, to start work by 5am, so I could do a 10 hour day for my client. I begged the radio clinic to give me either lunchtime appointments or the last appointment of the day so I could nip off to do the radio in my lunch hour or finish work at 3pm and head over there. I did it in an hour – I was only in the machine for 5 minutes. After the radio appointment I would come home and go straight to bed and sleep for as many hours as I could – often 10 hours. So for a month I did this cycle of getting up early, working, rushing to radio, going straight to bed, and starting all over again. Pure adrenalin and huge amounts of caffeine. On the days that a team member at work didn't show up because they felt a bit under the weather I was like... really? One of those moments where you realise how deeply embedded your Gen X work ethic is.

The chemo and radio are very different. The chemo was emotionally taxing, and hard on my body – but there were good weeks where I could get on with things, and the nurses in there were lovely. The radio was pure physical exhaustion that got worse as the days went on. There's something about the relentlessness of it – rushing to the hospital every single day. And it's so lonely in that room with all those machines. I couldn't bear it. On the first day when I realised they were walking out of the room and leaving me alone I just cried, and I had to ask them to talk to me through the process over intercom or I was going to have a panic attack. By then I'd done 2 surgeries and chemo and my central nervous system was just fried.

My whole body hurt like hell – everywhere – which I assumed was the chemo/radio combo. Was hard to walk around the house – my wrists and ankles were the worst. And nobody told me that for months after the radio I would have diarrhoea. I'm not sure if it's just me, but yeah that happened. I got a bit worried after a while, and then it stopped. I assume – have never asked anyone about this – that it's the body's way of expelling the radiation and the dead cells.

We'd been in total lockdown for 3 months by this time. The Melbourne lockdown was not like the other global lockdowns. We had police and military on the streets. We were completely isolated. I'd been on my own for months, all the way through chemo. The daily news wasn't optimistic at this stage, we all knew we'd be in lockdown for many more months. And it was winter. There wasn't a huge amount of optimism around.

I got through it with a LOT of help. I relied totally on meal delivery services to eat because I had no energy or time to cook. And I would have been lost without Jasmine from Loose Lead Pets (check them out here: https://www.looseleadpets.com.au/) who walked the

dogs every day. The dogs hated me for a few weeks of course and started acting up.

By now I had reached the point where I had nothing to say. I had started off really positive, and now it was just gruelling. I was realising I was really ill and I had nothing to say to the world that felt authentic. I sat at home and just processed WTF was happening. How did I get here? And what happens next? I have no fucking idea.

TIPS FOR RADIOTHERAPY

 MooGoo cream if you get burns from the radio.

 Soft bras or none if you feel comfortable.

 You can usually schedule appointments around work. I recommend asking for the final appointment of the day so you can get your work done first and then come home and go straight to bed.

THE AFT

Peaking for a powerlifting comp that didn't happen

Hey friends, it's been a while. Turns out cancer is an exhausting business.

So the chemo is done and I finished radiotherapy last week too. To celebrate I was meant to be doing a powerlifting comp this weekend, but as we're on total lockdown that was cancelled. So I did my deadlifts in my hallway gym instead.

I JUST DEADLIFTED 140KG!!!

The plan was to have a go at 130KG – my first heavy-ish lift since surgery in January – but it was much easier than I expected so of course I loaded up 140KG. The form could have been better but all things considered it came up ok. And then rather than doing what I really wanted to do, I did the grown-up thing and called it a day because my body still has a lot of healing to do and this day was just for fun.

And last week I squatted 85KG with decent form.

Looks like we're back in business!

Now to work out how to get the elusive 160KG that I've been circling for a couple of years. The awesome Femmy Ayegun just lifted 163KG at age 58 so I probably also need to think about raising my game... Onwards.

12   38   31

The delayed reaction

It looks as if the sorrow happens after the fact.

It's nearly two weeks since the end of radio, and it's only now that I have time to start processing.

Cancer is a never-ending set of medical appointments, or tests or treatments, or recovering from tests or treatments, or thinking about treatment options, and so on and so on. It's all-consuming.

I was diagnosed on 6 January 2020, saw my surgeon within 2 days, had my first surgery within a week and second surgery a week later. It was warp speed – I heard the word cancer and I just wanted that tumour out as fast as possible.

There hasn't been a moment to think: I've been immersed in the doing and the getting through it all and staying upbeat. And working at the same time.

Now I have time to process the facts: that I had cancer and cancer can kill you. I'm realising that at any moment death can just come and take you – in spite of all your best efforts to avoid it.

This life thing that we all take for granted isn't promised to anyone, you can be here one minute and gone the next. And there is literally nothing you can do about it – nothing. I've never thought about this before, not even for a moment. It's a huge fucking shock.

I'm crying the tears I've needed to cry for ages but that there wasn't room for: big grief tears, tears that shake your whole body. It's not a kind of grief I've ever experienced before – it's not like losing a partner or having something go wrong and feeling sad. It's facing the fact of my own death for the very first time. Realising there's an end to all of this. Maybe not now, but it will happen.

The tears come every single day. I might be in the bedroom, in the kitchen, I might be folding laundry, I might be cooking. I might hear a song. I might be busy at work. I might not even be thinking about cancer. It doesn't matter. The tears come anyway and I can't stop them. I have to stop what I'm doing and just cry. Most often I kneel on the floor and put my forehead on the ground until they stop. It's the best place to be. There's no need to pretend that I'm strong now, it's all just got to come out.

And then I get on with whatever I was doing.

My brain is broken

I think it's the double whammy of chemo and menopause – my brain doesn't work any more.

When I explain the symptoms to people they say 'oh yeah I get that too' but they have no idea what this is like. I get absences which can last up to 5 minutes. I have no idea who I am, where I am, what day it is. Literally nothing. It's a bit terrifying. Fortunately I did a lot of drugs when I was young and I'm used to this, or it would freak me the hell out. When it happens I just sit down and touch something solid to ground myself, I breathe and tell myself not to panic, that I trust my body will work this out, and wait until gradually it comes back: I'm Jane, I'm at home in Melbourne, it's Wednesday.

I have a problem with recognition of people too. I see people when I'm walking the dogs and they stop and talk to me, and I have no idea who they are. Are they someone I should be warm with because I know them or politely distant because I don't? Often there's not even a glimmer of recognition, other than I recognise the face. I find these encounters really really stressful. I try to keep the conversation vague and high-level to avoid appearing weird or saying something wrong, and find a reason to keep on moving as quickly as possible.

I can't remember anything from one second to the next – I'll have an idea and in a micro-second it's gone. I have no idea whether it will ever come back – it's not that feeling that the idea is close by and it'll come back in a minute, it's gone into the void. I get half way through a sentence and can't remember where I was going or how to finish it which I can manage in social situations but it's not great at work. I have to write everything down.

People tell me I'm repeating things – I have no idea what I've said to who. I give permission to people to tell me to shut up when I'm repeating myself. I call people by their dog's name. I'm always finding myself in a room without knowing why I went in there

I wonder if I'm getting Alzheimers, or dementia or if it's normal. I go online and google it. It seems to be a common experience.

Because of this I still won't drive. It doesn't feel safe – or pleasant. It feels important to know who you are and where you are and where you're going when you're behind the wheel of a car.

NOTE: As I edit this book 9 months later this has improved hugely. But I still don't like driving because of it.

26 JULY 2020

Lockdown notes

I've been dressing for work all year even though I've been at home. But standards have slipped – I broke my rule about not wearing Uggs outside the other day for the first time. And I've given up pretending that I don't eat chocolate every day. Or ice-cream.

I'm seriously the world's biggest introvert, and even I feel lonely for other people now. I've been alone for most of the year – even before lockdown I was on my own because I was recovering from surgeries – which means it's now 7 months of really limited contact. And because of the cancer and the risk of covid it isn't just that I've hardly seen anyone, I've hardly even touched another person. I realise there are a lot of people whose suffering is far worse.

As time has slowed down the further into lockdown we go I feel something that I can only describe as a strong awareness of the passing of time. It resembles nostalgia but it's something else and I can't put my finger on the right word. Maybe there isn't one. The

Germans probably have one. It's missing the feeling of being young and carefree. What if we never get to feel carefree again? What if we've had all the fun we're ever going to have and it's never coming back and this is how life is now?

I'm coping pretty well all things considered, but lockdown and losing work has triggered the fear I've always lived with – that after a lifetime of striving and working so fucking hard, you can still lose everything. You do everything the system encourages you to, but you never feel safe: at any time you can lose it all.

I've found myself pondering whether I've had enough fun in my life and whether I've been a good enough friend. I think the answer to both is no. I wish I'd spent fewer hours working and more time having good times. I hope there's time to put that right.

My world has become so small, I've found myself taking photos of the morning sun on my bedroom wall.

Hair well & truly on the way back

Eyebrows are still patchy though

2 AUG 2020

State of disaster in Melbourne — curfew!

"On 2 August, a state of disaster was declared and metropolitan Melbourne was moved to Stage 4 restrictions. A curfew across Melbourne from 8 pm to 5 am was imposed, a 5 km (3.1 mi) radius restriction as added, and other restrictions that had previously been applied only to selected postcodes were applied to the whole of metropolitan Melbourne. A permit system was introduced for any residents that still needed to travel to work outside of their 5 km radius."

So this is a first – I'm living under a curfew: no-one allowed out after 8pm.

I'm an early to bed person, even without cancer, so it doesn't bother me.

But it does feel like the world is closing in. How much longer can this go on for?

Interestingly at 8.01pm my brain starts telling me I need some chocolate and Rizla from the garage. I don't. It's just a reaction to not being able to go.

There's more panic buying in the shops.

Friends who live overseas in countries with more covid and lots of death are still going on holiday and doing normal things, and we're not allowed to leave our homes. It's very surreal.

I have cancer

I'm starting to realise that I don't like saying I
have cancer – it feels too definite.

Having something sounds permanent.
Some of my cells have cancer but I don't
have it – all of me doesn't have it.
I'm more than cancer.

6 AUG 2020

We just keep going

As our world gets smaller and smaller I keep
looking up. The skies here are epic.

It relieves the claustrophobia and helps me to
breathe.

It's a reminder that the sun still rises and sets.
Nothing lasts forever.

Final day on my client gig

End of project presentation – over zoom – to my
client based in Canberra with everyone remote
working.

Still loving turbans.

Last day earning money
for a while.

More grief

The grief keeps coming.

I'm not moping, I'm not depressed, I'm not even really thinking about anything specific. I'm getting on with my day and then suddenly there's all these tears. It's just waves of a really deep grief that comes from somewhere else. It's unstoppable.

At the moment it seems to catch me towards the end of a day.

I've started asking myself whether I made the best use of the day that's passed. I've never thought about this before. I've always assumed I have endless days in front of me, to use any which way. Now I know my time is limited I need to be sure that I used each day well. I ask myself every night now: Did I love my life today? And if not what am I going to do about it?

I let the tears flow because they have to come, they feel like cleansing for the soul. Holy tears.

And then I go back to working out how to have an awesome day tomorrow, and how I'm going to deadlift 160KG before I die, and wondering how many dogs is too many.

IT'S JUST WAVES OF A REALLY DEEP GRIEF THAT COMES FROM SOMEWHERE ELSE. IT'S UNSTOPPABLE.

My reasons have changed

I think about lifting differently now. I haven't lost all hope that one day I might make it back to the platform and set some world records. But I also have to accept that this may not be possible. Even if that doesn't happen, I can't give up now. My oncologist doesn't have much advice for me but every time I see her she says 'exercise every day Jane'.

So I have new reasons to lift: Weightlifting is one of the few things that's proven to help with cancer recurrence. It's true. It's also one of the most effective things for keeping body fat low, and my cancer feeds on fat so that's useful. And it's the single best thing for bone density, which I now have to think about with menopause.

Even if it wasn't for all the health reasons it gives me structure in a structure-less year and it's something I can control in this year when we all have so little control over anything.

Winter in Melbourne

Winter in Melbourne is often glorious. This year it's ridiculously mild and very beautiful.

Very lucky to live on this stretch of river, with trees and sky.

Hardly anyone ever around now – sometimes we're walking and it's just us.

Maggie

I was more excited than she was about this. My daily dog walks are a lifesaver. I don't know how anyone is surviving this shit without a dog.

Spring is coming

"EVERYTHING IS EVERYTHING
WHAT IS MEANT TO BE, WILL BE
AFTER WINTER, MUST COME SPRING
CHANGE, IT COMES EVENTUALLY"

~Lauryn Hill – Everything is Everything

After winter must come spring... change is coming.

Forcing myself out of my comfort zone

THE SAFETY IS IN ME

I was getting anxiety every time I left my house. I didn't feel safe anywhere except home.

It got worse when I left the neighbourhood directly around my house where I walked the dogs every day.

I started forcing myself out of my comfort zone – walking to places that made me feel anxious. When I felt the anxiety come I would just stop in the street and breathe, tell myself over and over I'm safe I'm safe I'm safe.

I would negotiate with myself – we'll just go to the next corner today and then we can go home, we'll go further tomorrow – and this way I would push a bit further each day. When the waves of anxiety came I would stop on the street, and just sit with the idea that safety is not a physical place, it's in me.

I didn't always manage it – sometimes the fear and the exhaustion would get a grip, and I had to just turn around and head back to safety.

In retrospect I realise it wasn't a psychological breakdown I was having. My body was really tired and all she wanted was to be at home.

My loneliness is killing me

There are days I could SCREAM. The claustrophobia, the monotony, the loneliness. The aloneness has become almost a physical pain in my body.

I can hold it together most of the time, but then I'll hear a song that reminds me of better times and people I love and I just have to cry. It happens a lot just before I train in my gym – I use music to get my energy up, so whenever I train I have to factor in a 30 minute cry on the floor for before I can lift anything.

I KNOW you can't live life on regret, but God I wish I'd spent more of my life having fun with the people I love.

Appointment with my oncologist

She tells me I shouldn't be this tired. The bit of me that's an over-achiever feels that I'm failing cancer somehow. The bit of me that's a pleaser feels that I'm letting my oncologist down, or that I'm wasting her time because I'm not doing this right.

Why are other people recovering faster than me?

What's wrong with me? What am I doing wrong?

She can't understand why I'm holding back on the endocrine therapy (to stop the cancer from coming back).

She says "Jane, the women I usually see with this cancer, they're a lot older than you. You have a lot of years left to live."

Delta!

Delta and I walk every day without fail.

We're not allowed into each other's houses, so walking is how we catch up.

We walk our arses off – 10K every day – we must have walked for hundreds of miles together to keep each other sane during this time. It takes the edge off lockdown and it's great exercise every day. Plus it means that even though I live on my own there's never a day that I haven't seen or spoken to another human being.

I'm not sure what I would have done without Delta all this time.

When I couldn't go shopping and there were no food delivery services she did my shopping as well as hers. She walked my dogs after chemo when I couldn't

get out of bed even though she has two of her own. She sat with me the day I was convinced I had covid and was going to die and had a massive anxiety attack. The day after each chemo she would set a timer and come over to help me with the injection in the stomach to stimulate the white blood cells. And she made me chicken soup when I could eat again.

One of my worst memories of the year was the day she had an anxiety attack and she asked for a hug. But I couldn't. There was covid in circulation and my immune system was still weak. If I could go back in time I would hug her so hard. But we didn't know then if this thing was going to rip around here the way it had ripped around Europe.

Love you Miss Delta.

28 AUG 2020
More afternoon naps

I still nap every single day without fail.
This is like one of those holiday shots that you take on a sun lounger except
we're not even allowed to leave our homes never mind go on holiday.
These vegan Uggs are the most useful purchase all year. They go with
everything – even fancy work clothes – posh jacket on top, Uggs on the bottom.
Most of my fancy shoes have been completely useless this year.

Chadwick Boseman dies

Today the news is full of Chadwick Boseman's death.

Although I appreciate the cultural significance of Black Panther, it wasn't ever going to be in my list of Top 10 best films.

But I cry like a baby when I hear the news. I cry all day.

I've avoided all news relating to cancer deaths all year but I allow myself to go into this one, I can't help it, I just fall into it.

By all accounts he was a beautiful man. He did charity work. He had faith.

I watch the video of his commencement address and it kills me: ""When I stand before God at the end of my life, I would hope that I would not have a single bit of talent left, and could say, 'I used everything You gave me.'

I don't believe in the God he talks about, but his humility is beautiful. There's no way I could stand in front of anyone and say I've used everything I've been given. Far from it.

What a selfish life I've lived. How little I have done for anyone or anything except myself. I feel ashamed.

I've done enough work to know that shame is not a helpful emotion. I simply note that it came, and that it was a messenger. Changes are needed.

nytimes.com/2020/08/28/movies/chadwick-boseman-dead.html

29 AUG 2020
Saturday

Saturday. But it could be any day really.
Wondering if we need days of the week any
more. One of the few times I wore a wig. I loved
the colour and enjoyed how I felt in it.
I thought I would LOVE doing wigs. But it was
too itchy on my head and too much to think
about. So I didn't bother.

10   35   9

159

Other people's thoughts

The sky right outside my living room window...

There's SO MUCH going on in the world right now.
I'm practising being aware of my thoughts and ideas and asking whether
they're mine or someone else's or the collective's.

I practise letting something go if it's not mine or it doesn't help.

I simply say to myself 'that's not mine' and it's gone.

Spring 2020

And I'm just happy to be here.

35   75   43

Still in lockdown

Our local station at rush hour. Should be heaving. Just me and the dogs.

I'm starting to feel guilty that I didn't go home to the UK. Covid is a complete shitshow in the UK, so many deaths. What if something happens to my mum and I didn't go home because I had cancer? Have I been selfish? What a fucking thing to even be thinking about.

I'm also realising how lucky I am. Watching the scale of human suffering around the world as a result of all the lockdowns is giving me a totally different perspective on my cancer. I'm ill, but I'm safe, I have a lovely place to live, I have people taking care of me, I have food, I'm not going to starve. There's people losing everything. It's heartbreaking. I can't help feeling like one of the luckiest people in the world. Any one of us who's making it through this with work, money, food, and friends, has won the life lottery. Major gratitude starts kicking in.

When the claustrophobia is too much I come outside at night and stand in my front yard just to breathe fresh air for 10 minutes and to remember that I am free.

So many months into lockdown we're at the point where no-one wants to do another fucking zoom call to have drinks or chat. We'd all rather just be lonely than do more zoom. Everyone withdraws into their own way of coping.

There's a strange sense of isolation too. People from other places – Australia and overseas – call and say "hey, how are you?" all bright and breezy, as if we haven't been in lockdown since March and there hasn't been an army presence on the streets. I realise they have no idea what's happening here and how crazy it is and how we're all going nuts.

EVERYTHING IS ENDING

This phrase shows up one day. It feels that this thing is going to leave nothing unchanged.

Everyone around me is making big life changes – moving to the country, setting up new businesses, moving interstate, having babies. Except me. I don't have those options. I feel jealous. I feel that I'm being left behind.

But this is my lot for now. It's my time to sit still, to recover, to be patient. There's nothing I can do apart from this.

4 SEPT 2020

I cry and then I dance

Cancer is a treadmill, every day, every week there's something, it's a full-time job.

When it stops the questions come: Am I going to die? How many years do I have left? There's something about the way my oncologist talks to me and treats me – she's worried for me. I couldn't bear to ask before, but recently I wrote and asked her directly "am I going to die early?"

There's a voice that says I don't want to die. In the heat of things – during treatment – I strove for equanimity: if it's my time soon I accept that. But now, there is this little voice that says I'm not ready, I've still got things to do.

I cry every day now after barely crying at all. I couldn't collapse during treatment, that just wasn't an option.

I'm allowing all of it now – everything that wants to come. They feel like necessary tears, not tears of self-indulgence or self-pity.

Every morning I remind myself that this day will never come again and I get to choose what kind of day I'm going to have.

I have a renewed sense of how great it is to just be here, alive. And of how much love I'm surrounded by. How grateful I am for all of it.

I've noticed that with this personal sorrow comes a deep connection to the sorrow of others. Which is a mixed blessing given how much death and loss and grief is circulating. It's almost too much to bear.

So every day I cry. And then I dance.

Being strong

When people say to me 'you're so strong' the bit of me that's a human woman conditioned to being overly-humble and self-effacing and not wanting to be too powerful in case it's off-putting for others wants to say 'no I'm not'.

But I am. And pretending I'm not strong isn't going to help me. My strength will get me through this. Might as well own it.

I notice though it's not the strong I'm used to, it's a new kind of strong that I'm not so used to just yet. It's a strong that is also graceful and accepting, where my old strong used to fight and try to control. Or maybe a better way to put it is that this strong knows when to accept and when to fight.

It's Jedi-Mind.

Bad lockdown habits

In years to come when people say what did you do in lockdown? My answer is going to be I smoked weed and ate Maltesers. I got through so many of these massive boxes. At the start I would make a box last 4 days, then it became 3, then at its worst it become 2 days. 2 days to eat all of these. Oh, and I used to have a rule where I wouldn't eat them until night-time. After a while it became "Maltesers for breakfast? Why I think I will."

What matters

Having had to let go of so many things this year I'm asking myself what really matters in life.

I have a suspicion it's not what I thought. I think the list of things that matter might be a lot smaller than I realised and that it might be as simple as having a roof over your head, food to eat, and people who love you.

I'm starting to ask what I really yearn for – not what my ego wants but what my heart wants. I think this too might be a shorter list than I thought: just being at peace with myself, who I am, the life I have. I realise what I really yearn for is to feel free, to feel loved, to die knowing I lived fully, that I was really really alive and loved. I'm craving less stress, less busy, more simplicity, more peace.

I'm starting to think I got it all wrong.

I would give my right arm to have all the people I love in the world in the same room as me right now – doing totally normal stuff – chatting, drinking, dancing, hugging. That's literally all I want.

I can't leave the house without this happening

I go to the hospital for a medical procedure – I can't even remember what it was for, I've had so many. I have photos of me in the medical imaging department so it would be a scan or xray or something.

I come home to this. All over the house.

I'm in The Age again

So The Age did another article on people in lockdown.

I'm not going to lie. I saw this photo and I was in agony all day about it. I just look awful. Ugly, tired, ill.

I hoped that no-one would see it. Fat chance. For several hours on the day of publication I was on THE FRONT PAGE of their web site. Everyone saw it. I had messages all day about it.

For months afterwards – months! – people would come up to me in the street and say I saw you in The Age. So yeah they all saw me looking like this.

Kind friends said "you looked great" and pointed out that the picture needed to reflect the hard times narrative in the article. I think they were lying. I did not look great.

Full article here: https://www.theage.com.au/national/victoria/where-are-they-now-revisiting-melburnians-in-lockdown-2-0-20200903-p55s2y.

THE [AGE]

Endocrine therapy/hormone blockers

Because my cancer is hormone driven my oncologist wants me on tablets that strip all the hormones out of my body. I think I'd be on them for 5 years – or more.

This massively accelerates the ageing process.

As predicted by her "You're going to have the worst possible symptoms Jane, I can tell" I had horrible symptoms even after taking them for less than a week.

It was like having a lobotomy – all mental functioning ceased.

They made me instantly depressed – and I'm not depressed AT ALL.

They made my body hurt like hell everywhere, and my pain threshold is extraordinarily low now – one of my dogs likes to wrestle but it hurts so much it makes me cry.

My knees and ankles swelled up and hurt so badly I have to get tested for arthritis. By the end of a day I could hardly walk and had to use walls to get around the house.

I felt pity for myself. Not self-pity, which is a maudlin and woeful state.

Just a sadness at observing what was happening to my body and at the same time acceptance – we'll have to find a way to make this work somehow, and laughing at myself when I had to hold on to things to move.

They also make your vajayjay hurt. Like she is so dry it hurts, and there's throbbing, and shooting pains.

I have a voice inside that says over and over "you don't need them".

I have no idea if this is divine guidance or my childish ego having a tantrum. I stop taking them.

I don't want to die and so I go and ask to try a different type of these things.

From what I understand the medical options to mitigate the worst effects of these things are anti-depressants and a form of valium. I don't mind taking valium but I don't feel good about anti-depressants. I've used them before when I was young and very depressed. I hear other women say it's fine, but there's something in me that just doesn't want to take them.

20 SEPT 2020

HOLY FUCK I JUST WASTED MY LIFE

The gift of having breast cancer is the clarity you get from realising you'll be dead soon: Most of what I thought mattered doesn't; The things I've spent time stressing over are irrelevant; Most of what I've spent my money on is just stuff.

Add in lockdown and you get a masterclass in realising life is not what you thought it was.

I've been experiencing nostalgia for months. Nostalgia and looking backwards isn't something I usually do, so it isn't a feeling I'm used to. I start digging out old photos, also something I never do. Scrutinising my younger self and wondering how I got here, ill, alone. Thinking about the choices I've made and the path I've taken.

There was a moment – and it was just that, a moment – when I was hit with the realisation that I've completely wasted my life. It was like being punched in the face. I thought to myself "bloody hell, I've wasted my life, completely wasted it".

I almost couldn't breathe – I was bombarded with memories and regrets, that thing that people talk about where your life flashes before your eyes – it was exactly that. Images of all the decades I spent working rather than living, chasing an idea of success, status, and money. All the years I spent wallowing in depression, not caring if I lived or died when I could have been doing something meaningful with my life or simply having more fun. What a huge fucking waste of a human life. I kept thinking 50 years! So much time I've wasted. I've actually squandered my life.

I felt sick.

How could I have got it so wrong? How did I not see what was in front of me?

And then I came back to the fact that I can't change any of it. I can only hope I have enough time to make up for it. And there is always now.

26 SEPT 2020

Lockdown was feeling hard this week

Not sure why. Everything felt like a massive drag.

27 SEPT 2020

Just because

Sometimes dressing up makes lockdown more fun.

Positive bowel cancer test

So I got a positive bowel cancer test, which I need like a hole in the head.
A friend and I joke that this is not a fashionable cancer like breast cancer.
No-one wants to talk about bowels.
The dark humour has really kicked in.

9 OCT 2020

Still walking the empty streets

End of Melbourne lockdown

It's the end of our long long lockdown. It's unexpected and strange but I feel odd. Jealous. Left behind.

Everyone else is (very slowly) getting back to normal. Going out for drinks, getting their hair done.

I'm still here, too tired to leave my house. Going for drinks is the last thing I can imagine.

Lockdown was tough, but we were all in the same boat. I'm not in the same boat.

One day the anxiety just stops

I've had crippling anxiety constantly for about a year. It came out the blue, never had it before. (See first diary entry)
I'm in the bath and I hear a voice that says "you don't need the Valium any more Jane, the anxiety is gone". I felt an energy leave my body. My heart actually – it left my heart. I felt lighter. I wake up the next morning and stop taking them.

NOTE:

Other than the odd day I haven't had to use valium since this day, after using it every day and not being able to function without it. My anxiety isn't gone in it's entirety – I still don't like driving, I don't like busy places, I don't cope well when

I'm too far away from home. But it isn't that omnipresent fear of impending death that anyone who has anxiety knows only too well. As long as I stay close to home and I don't put too much stress on myself, I can go weeks without thinking of myself as an anxious person any more.

It was only that night that I first connected the anxiety to the cancer.

I now think that the anxiety – that I interpreted as some kind of mental or spiritual meltdown – was actually my body screaming at me that I had cancer. And once she had my attention it stopped.

9 NOV 2020
Getting ready for comp in 3 weeks

2020 has finally caught up with me – today was the day I gave in and let my belt out a notch. All the months of #chemo when ice-cream was an essential food group. And lockdown when boxes of Maltesers were my best friend. I'll sort it out in 2021.

Today was an ugly and hard 130Kg for 12 reps. Only 3 more weeks of training and I get to rest properly.

#thepowerliftingdragon

17   21   13

Gastroscopy and colonoscopy

So back to the positive bowel cancer test. This necessitated a gastroscopy and colonoscopy.

I was high AF when I took this picture in the recovery room. They use propofol to put you out for it – the drug that killed Michael Jackson apparently. I felt so fucking amazing for a few hours – I was having massive cosmic visions, I felt like I knew the secret to absolutely everything. I tried so hard to hold on to them as they woke me up, but they went.

So no bowel cancer and no blood leaks inside, which is good news. But I had the world's worst drug comedown for weeks afterwards – exhaustion and so many tears. I missed all my final training lifts for comp.

The week before the tests you have to covid test and then isolate. So the whole week is just boring.

I'm lying in bed one night watching Netflix and Maggie decides that she's going to scale the fence in the yard and disappear off into the world. I've lived here 7 years and she's never done this before. I'm in isolation, but I jump over the fence in my nightie to get her – what else can I do? I scream at everyone to stay away because I'm in isolation, I grab my dog and jump back over the fence. I think I've broken my arm – the whole

thing swells up and the bone is agony to touch, but there's no way I'm doing another week of isolation. I take some Nurofen and suck it up. If it's broken I'll ask the hospital to look at it tomorrow after the procedure.

My whole body is trembling because I just got a ton of adrenalin dumped into my system. I'm so stressed and I've completely had enough of everything. I don't feel like I can cope with much more. I have a big cry. How long is this fucking cancer thing going to go on for? What if it never stops and this is my life forever now?

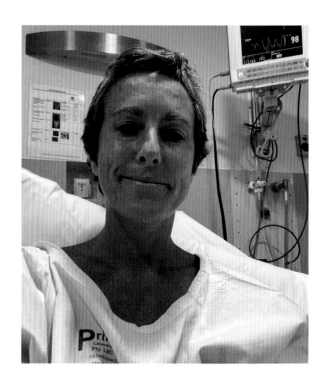

Last squat session before comp

Felt dreadful after the last hospital visit. My balance was all over the place, I was tearful, I was tired.

Was planning to squat 100KG today. Didn't happen. Just about pulled off 95KG for 5 singles. It is what it is.

14   33   11

Food is love

Today's a big day. It's been almost a year that I've been dependent on others for food. They would leave stuff on my doorstep in tupperware and I would leave the clean tupperware in my hallway to remind myself to return it. Today's the day the last bit goes home.

It feels a bit emotional. Partly being reminded at how much support came in the form of food, and partly a recognition that I'm back to being a functioning human being now.

My friend Robyn, who lives right across from me, has put the most delicious food on my doorstep for months, she just leaves it there, the way that women do. I particularly enjoyed her Ottolenghi phase. There's Jess, a friend I met whilst dog-walking, who brought me bags and bags of lovely things to eat. There's Beth, Trent, and doggy Herb, who came round after one chemo, with hand made pasta and pesto, cookies, and the best home-made ginger beer I've ever tasted. Because ginger is good for nausea. How thoughtful is that? My friend Henry arranged to have 3 different kinds of salted caramel ice-cream delivered one day because he knows I could only eat ice-cream after chemo, and that salted caramel is my favourite flavour. My neighbours Em and Milan left Weetbix on my doorstep because I was struggling with anaemia and it's high in iron. Mel, another neighbour, cooked me the most amazing lasagne for when I got home from hospital one day. A friend Miriam drove all round Melbourne looking for pasta when all the pasta had been panic-bought during the first lockdown, because pasta is easy to eat during chemo. Graham cooked me his special bread after every chemo so I could have beans on toast when I was ready to eat. There's a neighbour, whose name I don't even know, who regularly leaves bags of food on my doorstep. There's Mina, who left the best bread I've ever tasted on my doorstep, fresh out of her oven wrapped in a white tea towel. I got back from a dog walk and smelt it all the way down the street. There's Koto who cooked me the best gyoza I've ever tasted. And Delta who made me her chicken soup.

Food is one of the most useful and kindest things you can do when a person has cancer: it isn't just food, it's love.

The Powerlifting Dragon is back

This was the Melbourne leg of the 2020 Australian Masters Nationals. It had been cancelled 2 or 3 times by now.
I compete in the 50–54 years/58KG class.
My Insta post from this day:

Today was awesome in so many ways.

Squat was 100KG which is only 7KG off my best, and deadlift was 140KG only 10KG off. I'm pretty happy with that all things considered. I missed these numbers in training last week and nearly didn't compete because I had a bit of a tantrum and had to have a word with myself.

Total aside, it was just so much fun being in a room with other people again doing normal things after almost a year of lockdown and so many hospital visits. I hadn't realised how much I missed it. Even introverts have limits.

As always I owe it all to my awesome coach David Jame who somehow manages to get the best out of me in spite of my many health issues.

Hopefully I can get back to more competitive numbers next year.

#thepowerliftingdragon

17   48   37

WHAT I DIDN'T SAY

This was the first time I had left the house and got in a taxi and gone to a strange place on my own all year. My central nervous system was on total overwhelm – and I was still recovering from the gastroscopy/colonoscopy procedure a few weeks ago. I felt horrible.

The overwhelm produced tears – not that I didn't want to be there, I really did, but high emotions have to have somewhere to go, and so tears.

As I was warming up, I put my headphones on and hoodie up and just sobbed quietly to myself and hoped nobody saw.

When my coach arrived and asked me how I was I just said "I'm sorry but I'm probably going to cry all day".

I was also working hard to manage my own expectations. I had no idea if my energy would hold up for the day. I had to compete being entirely ok if I bombed every lift. I had to know this was a strong possibility. I'm a person who goes to win or to make records, so being willing to bomb was a big deal.

But something amazing happened, just as I was getting ready to go out for my first lift. Dave gave me the sign for 1 minute – time to start putting wrist straps on and getting ready to go out on the platform and squat. And as I was putting on my straps and focussing on the lift I was about to do, Cancer Jane disappeared and there she was – my alter ego the Powerlifting Dragon.

All my self-doubt just disappeared, I knew exactly what to do, and I went out and nailed the squat. The rest of the competition went really well after that. I made all my lifts despite missing all my final training lifts the weeks prior.

It was a real turning point for me after being at home on my own all year.

A bit of me came back. A bit of me that was nothing to do with cancer. The Powerlifting Dragon is still in the house!

Maybe all is not lost. (And I won my age/weight class.)

LIMN

ALITY

The liminality comes and I start writing poetry – of a sort

Liminality is the beautiful emptiness that comes after a major grief event. In liminal time our minds are quiet, there is a peace after the storm.

Out of nowhere I start writing poems – or something like a poem. I've never written anything like this before.

Only 1 person has read this book before publishing and her question was "were you high when you wrote these?". I wasn't. I stopped smoking weed a while ago. I was high on life. High on the awe that comes after you dealt with a life-threatening illness and took a look over the edge.

In this phase I spent weeks just staring out my window – at the sky, into the cosmos – completely overcome with awe at our existence in this universe. I suddenly understand mystical language and sublime art. They tap into something in us that's way deep beyond the ordinary, the mundane – they're the language of the soul. Ordinary words don't suffice.

I would wake up in the morning with a fully fledged set of words that would have to be written down immediately – or else they would disappear. Elizabeth Gilbert in Big Magic talks about this – how when inspiration comes you have to claim it or it goes to someone else to be expressed. They were finished as they arrived and usually only required minor editing.

They don't come any more. I read them now and I can't believe I wrote them. I couldn't even attempt to write them now. The moment has passed.

So yeah this is my poetic phase.

All is well

Around now my mantra becomes all is well and all will be well and all shall be well.

I just say it over and over in meditation in the morning. I find it really calming for my central nervous system.

It's inspired by Julian of Norwich I think, although I know very little about her except that she was a great British mystic who lived through the Bubonic plague, mostly in isolation. Her phrase just popped into my mind one day and I made it my own – hers was "All shall be well, and all shall be well, and all manner of thing shall be well." I take it to mean if we trust life and stay in love we can navigate anything that life throws at us – even the big stuff of life and death. We can accept it all with a glad heart.

It's easy to conceptually believe this when times are 'good' but so much harder to keep the faith when times are hard. I feel that I 'failed the test' during chemo, I just couldn't believe that all was well when I felt so awful.

I've realised it doesn't help me now though to believe anything else except that all is well. It feels better in my body, more peaceful to decide to give it all up and just say ok, this is what it is, and I'm going to try and to trust life, and trust love – to believe that all is well,

regardless of what happens next. I can't change any of it and so I might as well be ok with it. It's easier for me to live now believing that all is well.

I say to friends that I feel that I'm experiencing shock – a post-traumatic shock. I guess that at the time it was all too much to process, and now I'm being given pieces of the thing to wrap my head around. I get flashbacks – memories of things that happened that I've blocked out. Friends will say to me 'do you remember when....?' and I have no recollection of it at all.

And so I find this mantra really really soothing. It's all ok, it's all going to be ok. Whatever happens next, it's all ok.

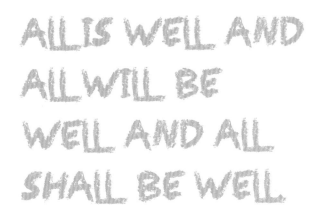

https://en.wikipedia.org/wiki/Julian_of_Norwich

Taking care of myself

Before cancer I had a whole regime of things...

- I would get up early to meditate every morning
- Take cold showers for my immune system
- Fast for all the health benefits
- Take a bunch of supplements; iron, magnesium and B12
- Have an epsom salt bath at night for magnesium and sleep

All through last year I just didn't want to do any of it. My body wanted lots of food, she didn't want fasting (especially during the radio last year – I couldn't get enough food in).

She definitely did NOT want cold showers, I couldn't meditate if my life depended on it, I can't stomach any of my usual supplements, in fact they make me retch.

And I can't do baths because the chemo and menopause in combination give me the worst hot flushes and baths just make it worse.

I just did what I had to do to get through each day and so long as I walked every day, drank loads of water, and slept as well as I could that was it.

I feel it starting to come back now. One day recently I felt like a cold shower in the morning to wake me up. My body started asking for less food. I woke up one morning and thought yeah I'm going to meditate today. I think it's the signs of normalisation.

25 DEC 2020
Christmas 2020

I spend Christmas on my own. I'm exhausted and I have nothing to say and the idea of making polite dinner table conversation terrifies me. I'm still at the point where I can't remember anything from one moment to the next and I zone out all the time.

When I'm with people I feel that I'm pretending – pretend smiling because I know I'm meant to smile at this moment even though I don't feel anything in my body, pretending I even have the energy or interest for it. So I spend the day alone and lie in the sun and it was a thoroughly good decision.

187

Being nothing & everything

As I move through life

I realise I know nothing

And the less sure I am, of anything

I care less, about fewer things

And yet I care more deeply about everything

I know I am something

But often I feel I am really nothing

I used to think that loving myself was important

Now I don't even care for that

It's too small of a concern

I love this life more than ever

But none of this belongs to us, we are simply visitors passing through

The thing is to not hold on too tight

So here I am

Not knowing and not caring

And I have never been more at peace

1 JAN 2021
New Years Day 2021

I've always loved the energy of new year – I love the chance to wipe the slate clean.

I meditated this morning and what came through was this: "It's time to stop fucking around Jane and pretending you're not what you are".

So that was pretty clear.

I'm not sure what that means practically – I think it's the call to do something meaningful before I die.

Menopause

I am really properly menopausal now – that is 12 months since last period. As soon as my cancer was diagnosed they took all my HRT off me and I haven't had a period since.

I haven't slept well since that happened. I wake up every single night now, around 1am, unbelievably hot and thrashing around trying to find a cold spot in the bed to put against my body.

Sometimes I get up instead. I was mooching around the house in the dark one night this week when it hit me that I am now considered undesirable. Past it.

The idea of this struck me as really really odd.

CANCER OR NOT, I'M JUST GETTING STARTED.

The urgent need to tidy up my life

I'm doing a radical overhaul of my life.

I just have to.

I'm de-stressing to the max. I can't/ don't/won't tolerate any stress whatsoever. I don't need it.

And I'm doing the house up. I'm making a home. I'm not feeling at all maudlin or depressed. In fact I've never been more clear or more happy. But if there's any chance at all of me being dead in the next 5 years I'm going to live in a nice house in the meantime.

I use the best crockery every day. I've thrown out all my underwear that's a bit past its best. I pay to have my sheets laundered and ironed every week so my bed looks fantastic every single time I get in.

I'm not saving anything for later any more.

Life is here today, now.

My dad

The day you realise your dad never made contact.

I've been so busy I only just thought about it.

We haven't spoken for a long time – maybe 15 years? Maybe more.

Don't you call when your daughter has cancer?

All I want now is peace

I just want a peaceful life, no stress, no drama.

It's not worth the price I would pay with my health.

I want to be one of the ones who makes it. I do.

I'm de-stressing my life.

I need to find a way to work/earn money that's not stressful.

But I also need to rewrite the internal story – the bit of me that likes stress.

I write a big note to myself and put it up in my office:

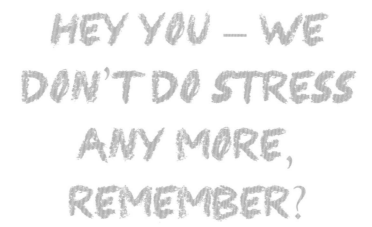

HEY YOU — WE DON'T DO STRESS ANY MORE, REMEMBER?

And then I realised that if I crave peace, so must everyone else – and if I want it for myself I must also be it for others.

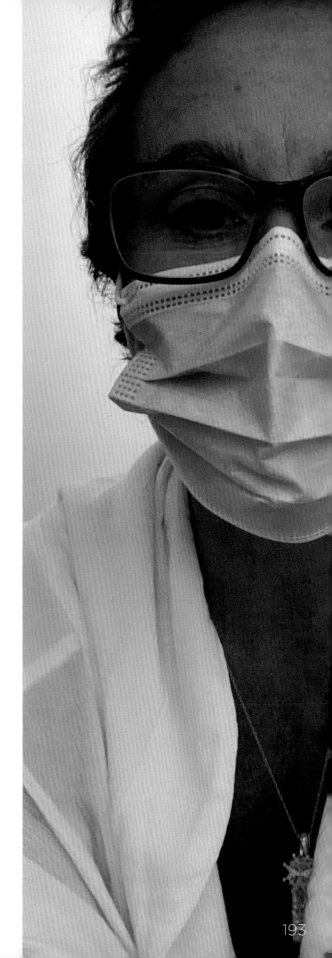

13 JAN 2021

First annual mammogram

First annual mammogram and CT scan today. I can't believe it's a year already.

The dude doing the CT scan says "that's Chantel's work isn't it?" when he sees the scar. She's famous for her needlework.

Both the technicians take their time doing their thing. I start to get nervous that it's bad news.

I don't get an urgent call from Chantel's office the next day so I assume it's fine.

I'm having to manage myself. I had an idea in my head that last year would be the end of this thing and that in 2021 I could get back to my life. I'm gutted it isn't working out like that.

I already have something medical almost weekly in the diary.

After this I need to go and see the surgeon to get the results. Next week I have the rheumatologist about the body pain. I'm doing cervical smear and skin cancer checks because I need to get everything checked now. We still haven't worked out if I'm anaemic so there's upcoming procedures for that.

I'm sick of being touched. I'm sick of being ill. I'm sick of being in hospitals. I'm sick of going for blood tests.

I'm tired. I want this all to be over.

193

16 JAN 2021

Bouffant

My hair is going through a phase. There was a while where it was hot like Sigourney Weaver/Sinéad O'Connor, but I think we can all agree that's no longer the case. Spoke to my bestie @brixtongrammar in London last night and we spent the first 5 minutes comparing my bad cancer hair with his bad lockdown hair. It's a close call but I do think mine is marginally worse.

14   21   12

Positive thinking is not where it's at for me now

I've realised what my problem is with positive thinking
It usually means if I think positive I'll get the outcomes I want
Or, if I'm a good person, I'll get the outcomes I want

As if life cares about the suffering or desires of one person
In cancer you might not get the outcomes you want

I have found it more useful to seek grace in the face of adversity
To be able to accept what I can't change
And to look for the pearls in the muck

Grace

Grace is not a word I ever used before cancer
Or a feeling I ever invited into my life
It's become important

I'm struggling with some big questions
What if I've wasted my life and I don't get a chance to make it up?
What if I'm one of the ones who doesn't make it?

I turn to grace
Grace in the face of these enormous things that I don't know what to do with
I don't know what I'm doing, it just feels right

I am nothing & nobody

I'm experiencing the greatest peace I've ever known.

My mind is so still, I'm barely thinking, it's so very quiet inside.

I feel that I'm as big as the universe, possibly bigger.

I have the most glorious feeling that I'm really nothing and nobody.

I wonder if I even exist? Is the thing I know as Jane real?

I know I'm here, but I'm not thinking or feeling anything: so what am I?
I've always thought I'm my personality, my thoughts, my ideas, but even without any of them I'm still here.

It can't be a coincidence that I don't feel that I'm any of those things any more and at the same time I'm happier than ever.

I try to do hill sprints

Trying to get fit again, and I feel the need to sweat out the chemo and radio.

I had always done hill sprints as my cardio.

Now, my body hurts everywhere – not sure if it's menopause or the hormone therapy. My feet and ankles are the worst of all.

I take up spinning instead

Best decision ever. I get to sweat without leaving the house to go to a gym and it doesn't hurt my body.

Once I start tracking my heart rate I realise my body might not be finished. Although I've put a lot of fat on (not good for hormone based cancers – did you know the body can make hormones from body fat?) my heart and lungs still work.

Feels good to know that.
Gives me loads of confidence.

Other people and me

These days

The world feels a long way away

I can't reach people

Or they can't reach me

Either way

We're operating in different dimensions

And there's no bridge

Or translation device

We end up talking at cross-purposes

Both frustrated

I can't give them what they want

I tried for a while

But I'm sick of defending how I feel

Or explaining how hard cancer is

And pretending to be well when I'm not

I pull back

This is what it is for now

Pillcam

Did you know there is a camera the size of a massive pill that goes all the way through your body and takes photos to see if you have problems in your gut? I didn't either. It's called Pillcam. It's all in the name.
Another day fasting and at the hospital.

There is nothing wrong with me.

I know they're trying to help me, but I'm so sick of hospitals and blood tests.

18 FEB 2021

At the rheumatologist

The endocrine therapy (tablets to stop the cancer coming back) have made my body hurt so bad we're now testing for rheumatoid arthritis. I know nothing about this, and then I research on Google and think I definitely don't want this on top of everything else. It looks awful.

We do blood tests.

The good news is I don't have it.

The bad news is that the pain is a side-effect of the endocrine therapy, the therapy my oncologist very much wants me to take, but we now know it makes my body hurt as badly as if I had rheumatoid arthritis.

I have so much awe at just being alive

I want to sit with this feeling forever
Never move from this place in which I sit
And just enjoy how this feels
I don't want to fill the space with the noise and stuff
and doing of life
This is all I could ever need

Life is meant to break you

I think that life is meant to break you
It's the only way we learn
And the stronger the personality
The more control we try to exert
The more we resist being broken
The more we need it
At least this is how it is for me

Awestruck by life

I spent my whole life being busy, achieving things, and searching for some grand purpose. Now I prefer doing nothing, I don't care deeply either way about a lot of things, and I don't even have anything to say most of the time. I enjoy being unburdened of all that ego and ambition, of caring about everything and having opinions. It was exhausting.

It's not that I've given up, it's more that I feel awestruck. At how close life is to death – the idea that we are here and then we can be gone. And there's a deep reverence too. For the mystery that is life, and because in all of it I am here, being me.

No words make sense. All you can do is be still and allow it to take you where you where it will.

How do I explain?

How could I possibly ever explain to you, who have not experienced this, that I am on the ride of my life?

A cosmic adventure into the mystery of life and death.

I have never been so fucking tired

I think it's me

I'm not doing enough of the right things

And then I read about post–cancer fatigue – it's a thing.

I reckon I'll be recovering all year.

I'm using so much caffeine to get through a working day it's disgusting.

I just want to not feel tired.

Would I say yes to this if...

...I was going to be dead in 5 years? I ask myself this question every single day now – about everything.

One upside of having cancer is realising there's a finish line to all of this – we all have our allotted days and that's it, game over.

I don't intend to waste any of them anymore doing things I don't want to do, or things that don't make me feel good. I wasted too many already.

It's very liberating, especially for women who aren't used to saying what they want.

I'm practising saying no. No, I don't want to do that. It feels strange.

I'm practising hearing my own no – the no that comes from somewhere deep in the body or the subconscious – and not ignoring it, which is what I used to do. No. I don't want to do that.

It's not done

I thought it would be over by now. Done. I think I thought I could bring my strong achievement-orientation to cancer.

But it's not. Far from it.

The fatigue is awful. I would guess another year of recovering to get back to anything resembling the person I used to be. I work, walk the dogs, and go to bed. That's the totality of my life. I feel so tired I'm hallucinating, I feel that I'm going mad.

I've had to check out from most of my friendships. I feel the judgement or disappointment of others and there's just too much friction. I might be about to lose more people from my life. I've got nothing to say and I'm too tired to want to do anything, and nobody seems to understand how this feels.

I still don't like driving, I don't have fast reactions in me. I don't like being in the city or anywhere busy or noisy. My central nervous system is on edge all the time. I don't really want to be anywhere but home.

I haven't had a good night's sleep for over a year. Menopause wakes me up at 2am so hot I don't know what to do. I'm going mad with exhaustion. I'm at the hospital or doing tests almost every single week still – although I think that might tail off soon.

Maybe this is just my life now, maybe I'll never be the same. Will I ever have fun again?

Going back to normal

It seems to be expected that I'll go back to normal.

I feel the subtle expectation of others, the judgement that perhaps I'm being a bit slow in coming back to normality, or a bit negative about it all. Why don't I want to come back to their normal?

But for me there is no going back.

A door closed on a version of me and a time in my life some time ago.

I'm glad of it.

Can you be happy without needing to achieve anything?

Having breast cancer was illuminating to say the least. I thought I had my addiction to achievement under control, and I had had a really strong spiritual practice for years. I thought I knew what's up.

I got a massive shock when I was forced to think about death for the first time, and I realised that none of what I thought mattered actually matters. Not the house I spent years working to pay for, not the clothes or any of my stuff – it will all just be junk when I'm gone. And most of the things I sent my time on didn't matter either. I realised I've spent my life addicted to busy and achievement, buying stuff, and not really living.

A lot of us are trapped on the hamster wheel of not–enoughness – I'm not enough, I don't have enough – which keeps us always chasing more. We live in a system that keeps us in a permanent state of dissatisfaction, the thing we're chasing always just out of reach. And so we never stop.

We think the point of life is to achieve something. Maybe the point of being alive is simply to be alive? To just enjoy the simple fact of being here, and being you, and having this life.

Can you be happy sitting on your own in an empty room, without needing to do or achieve anything at all?

7   38   25

How will I love my life today?

Before cancer I used to start every day filling every single moment in my diary with something to do. There were also plans for the week, the quarter, the year. There was even a 5 year and a 10 year plan. I lived my life as if it was a to-do list. I had a list of lists.

When I got cancer I realised there's a finish line to life. It was a holy shit moment. If I die soon and all I've ever done is tick things off my list what kind of life is that? I'm done with rushing around all the time. I like doing less now, and moving more slowly. I just don't enjoy days anymore where you're stressed all day because you have too much to do. I used to get high on that shit. It's an addiction.

Now... while there are still things I want to do and I still have to work, I also ask myself how can I love my life today? How do I use this day well?

Realising there's an end to all of this I don't intend to waste even one of the days I have left. There's no more filling my life with stuff that doesn't make me feel good now and putting off happiness until later.

I make sure there is something in every single day that remind me how much I love my life. It might be as simple as speaking to someone I love. It might be a great session in the gym. It might be sitting in the sun for half an hour. It might be creating something or doing some writing. Doesn't matter what it is – work or home – but there has to be something I get pleasure from, that's more than doing things that I have to do.

This question also brings a different quality to things. We all have to clean the house, do shopping, cook, and put the bins out. We have to do stuff we don't enjoy. But now I try to enjoy these things. I have to do them, I might as well enjoy it right? Or else I'm not enjoying my life.

I did gratitude practices for a lot of years and used to wonder why they didn't always work, and why they all felt so silly. I didn't realise that just being here is completely miraculous. That in this vast universe here I am – this unique spark of consciousness, living, breathing, creating, loving. That's the thing to be grateful for.

What I need at this point in my life are more ephemeral things like being at peace with things, and having more fun. Not rushing around! Maybe what I need is to just sit in the sun for half an hour.

I don't want to get to the end of all this and find that all I've ever done is spend my days on my to-do list. That's not living for me. I don't have time to waste any more – from here on there isn't to be a single day that I didn't enjoy the simple fact of being alive. Fundamentally I'm happier when I have more space in my life and I'm not rushing around creating my own stress. My idea of a good day is no longer judged by my productivity.

One year after chemo

I'm not really looking backwards at the moment but I woke up this morning and FB reminded me it was a year ago I started chemo. The strange thing is that none of it feels real. I still don't really believe I had cancer. I look at photos and I don't connect to the person in them.

When I have to say to people I had cancer it sounds wrong. It couldn't possibly be me. I also have no idea how I managed to do it all – treatment, working, lifting, lockdown, writing a book. It was nuts.

Anyway, shortly after this I lost my hair and now a year later I look like a microphone. I hope better hair days are coming...

7   38   25

I want what I want

For the first time in my life

I want what I want

I don't want something else

I want exactly what I want

Even if you don't like me for it or you walk away from me forever

I'm not negotiating any more

It makes me feel unreasonable

When I want what I want

But it's all I've got now

I write this after having an argument with an uber driver. I've lived where I've lived for 7 years, I know every road from the city and which to take at certain times of the day. I ask to go a certain route because the other routes are all horrendous at 5pm on a Friday. He wants to go a different way. He argues at me for 15 minutes. Before cancer I would have folded and done what he wanted. I will not fold today. We will go the way I want to go.

In the end the route we go doesn't matter – what does matter is my ability to express what I want – for the first time in my life. I didn't go through everything I just went through to not want what I want and to ask for it.

The changes in me

I don't feel like me any more.
I don't feel much about anything.
I don't care about anything.

I can't dance. I've lost my rhythm my
sensuality my connection to my body.

Training is hard. I used to enter the gym ready
for anything, loving the struggle, the harder
the better.
Now my internal voice says I'm not sure i can
do this, my body hurts.

My confidence is gone.

I don't drive.
I hate the city.
I feel that I might never have sex again.
I don't know who I am now.

16 MARCH 2021
Seeing life as it is

I'm struck by the enormity of things – life, the universe, time
It's so vast our small human minds can't even begin to understand it
In the face of this I feel so utterly insignificant – in the best way
I don't think it's meant to be taken as seriously as we do
I think we're supposed to enjoy it more

17 MARCH 2021
True Story

One day as you prepare to face your death you will look back and
wonder why you spent so much of your life working and worrying
about things that didn't matter and buying stuff you didn't need –
when you could have been loving your life instead.

18 MARCH 2021
You don't understand

Until you've had cancer – or some other life–threatening illness – you don't
understand.

Stop trying to tell me how to feel or what I should think.

You have no idea.

Devotion

If you have to talk about self-love and self-care

You neither love nor care for yourself truly

You're a woman trying to find reasons to care

Wondering why you can't seem to find a reason

The thing is, you must come home

Allow your hard edges and your wounded parts to melt

Dare to know yourself as something cosmic and wonderful

In that place you find devotion

And no reasons are needed

I don't know how to live my life now

I might be dead in 5 years.
But I might live til I'm 100.
How do you live your life with 2 such contrasting future scenarios?
I have cake with a friend.
He quotes Gattaca: "I never saved anything for the swim back".
I cry. It's good advice. Just go all out every day and let it take care of itself.

Sometimes I forget

Sometimes I get lost in my misery
And I forget that everything that matters
to me came from darkness
I have to remind myself
That this is exactly where I want to be
This place that is both devastation and
ecstasy

I have met my death and it doesn't scare
me
But the knowing
That all my defences against life are
useless
Is equal parts freedom and free-fall
And I have not yet learnt to steady
myself in this place with no ground

I have no use now
For my excuses my untruths my
smallness
There is a weight in my chest
A longing to be consumed

I ask for annihilation in the way of Teresa
of Ávila
A burning spear through the heart
But maybe it is not my time
This is not a goal to be achieved
It is a thing bestowed
When we are ready
Patience has never been my strong suit

I wrote this when I was thinking back on the chemo stage and how hard I had found it.

I know from years and years of doing spiritual work that I have to go into the darkness to find the light. I know this. I've learned it over and over.

And yet I allowed myself to get lost along the way. As the chemo did its work and the isolation of lockdown kicked in I would sometimes fall into fear. I forgot to trust myself. I lost my faith in life. I forgot that I signed up for this arduous journey and all the ways in which it would break me. I wanted it and then I forgot. Physical body discomfort and pain easily distracts us from what we really want and derails the best of spiritual intentions.

Upon reflection though this was the most powerful part of the journey– the stripping back of everything that chemo is, going all the way into the darkness of it, the initiation of the hair loss and being removed from human contact was actually transformational. These were the Rites Of Passage, this was me in the deepest darkest parts of the journey Into The Forest. This is what I signed up for at the beginning of things. What was happening outside was also happening inside. It was forcing me to let go of layers upon layer of myself that had outlived their usefulness. And it was because of this, that the whole experience became so powerful. I got the annihilation (of ego and my small fearful self) I asked for.

I love this pain

I love this pain
It's a hot line to my own tenderness
A softness that doesn't come so
easily to me
It's too female
And I've never claimed her
Until now

I love this pain
It's beautiful, it's real
The heavens opened
And said here have this
The awesome of all the cosmos
Our gift to you
I want to sit with it and hold it close
Before the heavens close
And I fall back to earth

I love this pain
It's ecstasy
I think grief and love are the same now
That the purpose of grief is to spur you
to love and to live
I'm more alive than I've ever been

I love this pain
It's the biggest thing I've ever done
What's the rush?
Allow me to linger
I want to be sure it breaks my heart
I will not leave until I know it's done

That is why we are here

LOOKING BACK

I wrote this when I felt the grief phase was starting to diminish and I had the huge realisation that I didn't want it to end. There was so much about it that was beautiful – it was exquisite. I didn't feel sad, I felt alive, never closer to the true meaning of life. I loved how it felt.

The door will close on this experience soon – I feel this – and I don't want to waste a moment of it, doing normal life stuff – that will all be there later. There is nothing I want more than to sit here with my tender heart in my hands and revel in how I feel. I want it to break my heart open, to walk out the other side of this utterly transformed. Otherwise what was the point?

Please stop asking me if the cancer is gone

Please stop asking me if the cancer is gone

I don't know, they don't know

For now they can't see it

But there isn't a test in the world that can say for sure

That you no longer have cancer

And it's not coming back

It could be hiding somewhere, waiting, coming to get me later

I know you want it to be true

But what you really mean is tell me you're not going to die

Please

So that I can stop worrying about you

And not have to think about death

I can't relieve you of that worry

My reality is that I'll always be wondering

I would be lying to myself if I told you everything was fine

And I can't do that to make you feel better

I have chosen to sit with the reality of things

And to not pretend

That things are anything other than as they are

I'm not sure of anything any more

All the things I was so sure of

I'm no longer sure of

And I like it

Ego tantrums

I'm realising that the death grief is also
an ego tantrum

Knowing that death can just come and
take you – that you are powerless to
stop it

That must be the ultimate snub for a
human ego

I'm laughing

Me and my oncologist

"You look better than I've seen you look in ages" she says as if my looking bad was because I had let myself go, rather than because she had poisoned me half to death.

For a moment I was offended.

And then she smiles a huge smile and says "I didn't want to tell you this before but I've been really worried you had stomach and bowel cancer and I'm pleased to tell you you don't". I had noticed that I kept being sent for increasingly more invasive and costly procedures, but was too tired to ask.

I realised how invested she is in keeping me alive, and I feel bad for all the times I was that surly patient who was angry that chemo and radio is the only solution to cancer, as if that's somehow her fault. I must apologise the next time I see her.

We have a complicated relationship.

I made her promise upfront to always tell me the truth. She's been true to her word. When I tried to negotiate my way out of chemo we did some tests to see if I could get by without it – her opening line on delivering the results was "it's the worst possible news Jane". Me and my friend Graham still laugh about this. Even after these results I was still negotiating – what if I eat well and exercise more and destress my life? "Yes but you did all those things Jane and you still got cancer". That shut me up for a minute.

Now I'm trying to negotiate my way out of the meds to stop the cancer coming back because they make you feel like hell. She doesn't understand why I would ever not take them: "If it comes back Jane and it's in an organ it's automatically stage 4 and then there is nothing I can do for you".

She tries to coax me into taking the meds I don't want to take. Now we know I don't have rheumatoid arthritis and that the first lot of hormone therapy almost crippled me, she tries to get me on a second tablet. "We've got to hit you with these soon Jane. You have a high risk of the cancer coming back. More than 3 in 10 chance". She says that every time I see her, multiple times each visit. I wonder if she thinks I've forgotten?

WE SPEND OUR VISITS CALCULATING MY CHANCES OF BEING DEAD WITHIN 5 YEARS. THERE'S MY 31% CHANCE OF RECURRENCE MINUS 8% BECAUSE I DID THE CHEMO AND IF I TAKE THE MEDS WE CAN SUBTRACT ANOTHER 10%.

I'm not sure I'm going to take them. I don't want to take them. There is still the voice inside that says you don't need them.

But the wife of a friend came over recently and was kind enough to share that her sister had breast cancer, it was gone for 10 years, and when it came back she was gone in 18 months. I wonder if this is one of the messages from life that I would look back on from my deathbed and think "the universe tried to send me a message and I didn't listen".

Because my oncologist is so persuasive and on the back of this story, I try the second lot. I always say yes even though I hate them. It's the pleaser in me.

I really try. I really do. I promise myself, whatever happens, I'm going to take them for 2 weeks.

I take half a tablet not the full dose because the first lot were so awful. They take my brain functioning away and I can't work. I hate them.
I make 4 days and then give up.

26 MARCH 2021
Chemo curls

I learn this week that there's a thing called Chemo Curls. Women with straight hair can find their hair grows back curly after chemo.

This is them. My hair has always been straight.

Apparently they might grow out.

I kind of like them but I don't know what to do with them and so I just look old and frumpy. Very unsexy. I feel a bit embarrassed walking the streets and I look awful on zoom.

Soon it will be winter and I can hide it in beanies until spring.

Not knowing

There's a lot of not knowing in cancer

I'll never know for sure why I got the cancer

I don't know for sure if it's coming back

I can never know if any of the treatment I did helped or not

I won't know if any of the stress of the last year has affected my chance of recurrence

I don't know what to do to be sure to stop it coming back: will food, exercise, and meditation make a difference?

I don't know whether taking the meds to stop it coming back will work, or whether my not taking them is going to take me to an early death

I don't know how to live now that nothing is the same

So what do you do with all that not knowing?

Trust yourself to work it out

Get up every day and keep living

Sit with the cosmos and know that in the end all is well

Full Moon

It's Full Moon and I feel slightly mad

I feel a weight on my heart

I am craving being broken

It's what needs to happen

To finish this thing off

I could scream

I wish I wasn't so British

I'm willing to give up everything

But I know that the more we want it

The further away it goes

That we must sit with the desire and the frustration

And allow it to come when it is time

I don't know anything

But I know there is a point to this

I will wait

Easter

Over Easter, the time of resurrection, another part of me came back online.

I can't describe exactly what piece it was, it wasn't dramatic, it was just a subtle sense of feeling a bit more like me again.

Maybe it was because it was time for this to happen. Maybe it was a week off work and lots of sleep.

Whatever it was, there was another piece of myself to gather up and welcome home.

A place between worlds

You go to a different world – a place between worlds
And I'm alone
Everything is different here, unfamiliar
I am becoming different here, unfamiliar
Others cannot understand
They simply cannot
Don't even try to explain

I was angry for a while – at the aloneness
Where are my people?
And then I came to understand
That this is a solo walk
No-one *can* follow you there
They go when it's their time

In this place we take account of our life
A great reckoning
Our memories
Our shortcomings
The ways in which you failed others
The ways you failed yourself
The regrets
The heartbreaks
The ways in which we were not loved, or were not
loving

There is no pretence no artifice here
No protection from the truth
it is not loving – it is what must be done
You are eyeball to eyeball with life
(Which is really You)
As she guts and disembowels you
And says this is for your own good you know
This is your chance
To make peace
With all that you are and all that you've been

I no longer think of hell as the place we go after we die
It is this place
Where you go to forgive your human self
On the way to finding grace

Grace is something I've never experienced
It's beyond human
A field of cosmic love
It appears on the path in times of need
You have to ask to know it though, don't forget to ask
You must let the cosmos know your heart is here for it
In grace all is well and all is forgiven
Is this God?
This place where nothing is wrong, all is well, and all is
forgiven
I feel it might be

I think there are 3 phases to this thing
It starts with the regret and a pain so great it stops you
from breathing
This is not a time to collapse or flinch
It's a time to stand tall, look it in the eye, and let it have
it's way with you
Know – that it will pass and you will be better for it
And then when it has wrung you out
Now you sink to your knees
Sit in stillness
Hold open the empty space inside of you
And allow the awe, the love, to ever–so–gently take you
over

Enjoy this, this is an ecstasy that is beyond words or the
comprehension of the human mind
Take every last bit in – it doesn't last, it cannot, eventually
you must get back to things
As you feel the intensity subside it is replaced by clarity,
simplicity, and straight–up joy
A resolution to waste any of your days
You are ready – to get on with being here, being you
It's a new day

When I closed
I swear I
I felt that I was
That I was
And yet
I think this is
mystics talk
There are

my eyes last night
touched infinity
vast beyond words
nothing at all
everything
what all the great
about
no words

I have a cold & it feels great

I have a cold for the first time in ages. It's so nice to be ill with a plain old common cold. I didn't have to worry if it's going to kill me, I didn't need to go for blood tests. No hospital visit. It was just a cold and I didn't give it a second thought. A return to normality. I've thought about cancer all day every day for almost a year and a half.

The oncologist

We've ruled out 2 of the endocrine therapy options.

She now wants to explore Tamoxifen.

I am reminded again of the "More than 3 in 10 chance of recurrence.".

It makes me smile now.

I know she has my best interests at heart.

I want to tell her I'm not taking them.

But I'm not completely sure that this is my decision – and she's so persuasive.

I take away a third prescription and agree to try them.

NOTE:

My oncologist tells me the literature says that 40% of women stop taking the endocrine therapy for the same reasons as me. I find it comforting to know this – it's not just me who's struggling. (Note I'm not making a recommendation.)

My birthday: 52

I'm not a huge fan of birthdays but I do find they tend to bring change. I woke up today and thought 'I want to go out for drinks tonight' – one of those glimpses of my old self that I get from time to time. A friend said 'don't wear one of those kaftans Jane wear something sexy' but I have no idea what sexy is any more, so I wore jeans and a t shirt and no make-up. I actually enjoyed being out – and no anxiety. Small steps, big progress.

I'm definitely at the end of a phase. The emotional intensity isn't what it was, I think most of the grieving is done. It's time to transition into something else, the next phase, whatever that is. It's time to trust that it's ok to stop – to know that I did what I had to do and I made it. I did it. I made it.

It's a long road back from cancer, it's not like having a cold or something where you wake up one day and think to yourself "I feel better now". It's very very slow and incremental, with the increments so small it can feel that nothing is really changing.

I'm still so tired – this year is as tired as I've ever been. The tank is completely empty. I do what I can each day and then I stop. There's something really nice about this though – after a lifetime of rushing around now I stop when I'm tired. I've decided to give myself the winter off work to hibernate and to rest finally.

My world has become very small. I still don't like driving much and I don't like being away from home. I still feel that people are a long way away and even with friends I often don't know how to build the bridge. I pretend at normality sometimes because I want to maintain friendships. I don't feel any need to be in the world, I've got nothing to prove, nothing I need to do or say. And I'm ok with this for now.

My memory and cognitive powers are still really poor. I can't do mental arithmetic – I can feel the gears trying to grind, I get stressed, and then I have to stop. And I still can't hold anything in memory for more than a second – I have to write everything down immediately or it's gone. I rely heavily on voice memos.

I still haven't decided whether or not I'm going to take the hormone therapy.

There are days that sadness comes – days when it's so much I don't know what to do with it all. What am I sad about? Often it's not clear, it's more a pervasive sense of loss on a fundamental level. Sometimes it's a death sadness: I don't want to have to let go of life yet.

I feel that I don't know anything about anything any more. So much of the world that used to interest me just doesn't now. I find myself scrolling Netflix and finding nothing I want to watch, and scrolling news sites or social media and finding very little of interest. The list of things I care enough to get annoyed about or to spend time thinking about is a lot smaller. All the things I used to care about and worry about – just gone. Memories of the past – all gone. I don't really know who I am now, what I care about, what I want to do. This is in part disorienting, but there's a sense of freedom too. I feel unburdened, empty in the best way. I absolutely love how this feels. I've never been more at peace with myself and with life.

I have no desire or interest in 'going back to normal'. My old normal is gone – there is no way back. It wasn't healthy, it was a lot of stress and I can't have stress in my life anymore, it'll kill me. It's as simple as that. I still want to achieve things, create things, I don't think I've completely given up, it's just that the old way isn't for me now. Anything that disturbs my peace now is a hard no. I've noticed I laugh more now.
I feel that I'm really here – more in my life than I've ever been.

IT'S TIME TO TRUST THAT IT'S OK TO STOP – TO KNOW THAT I DID WHAT I HAD TO DO AND I MADE IT. I DID IT. I MADE IT.

RECO

VERY

MAY – AUGUST 21

Time to rest

May

I've taken 6 months off work to rest. I'm utterly exhausted. Post-cancer fatigue (no-one mentioned it). I'd kill for a holiday somewhere hot with a sun lounger and a view of the ocean. But it's winter here now and with covid/ continued lockdowns in Australia there's no such thing as a holiday.

It's more than that: it's a mindset. I've been running hard for 18 months. I know it's time to say to myself "it's ok, we did it, we made it" but it's difficult to make this transition. There's a bit of me that doesn't feel safe enough yet to allow myself to stop. What if something else comes up? What if the cancer hasn't gone? How do I give myself permission to stop running and to rest?

I make a plan for the next few months: sleep, meditation, training, sort out my diet, de-stress, not doing much and enjoying it. Why this needed a plan I don't know, but that's me.

I notice that I have energy enough to do 1 big thing and a few small things each day before my body wants to stop. I'm not forcing anything, I stop when I need to. I meditate in the morning, potter around and do a few things, have a nap, walk the dogs, have a bath and go to bed. I'm in bed at 6pm, sleep for at least 10 hours and do 2 daytime naps. I don't care if it's not cool, I want to feel better and sleep is my friend. I tackle the hideous amount of sugar I've been using and that feels good. I was never a big drinker but I've cut it out almost entirely now: the oncologist was really firm on

no alcohol and suddenly the news is full of articles about the link between cancer/breast cancer and alcohol. I start doing deep tissue massage that gets right into the scars and my ribcage. I feel sick for 2 days but the emotional and physical release feels good. I do some infra-red saunas too because they're meant to be good for detox: I get headaches and weird disturbed sleepless nights afterwards, almost like visions. It's unpleasant, verging on scary. Must be processing something big. I plan to buy one for home so I can do it every day.

I'm gradually starting to process the shock of it all. But I haven't had a day yet where I just feel like me. Hard to explain that sentence. I feel that I'm in a bubble of cancer and not back in the world yet. And my brain is still offline. It feels that my body is coming back faster. I hope this isn't a permanent state, I need my brain for work.

But things are definitely trending up slowly. I woke up one day last week and decided I felt safe enough to drive my scooter for the first time – the first time in over 18 months that I felt able to. And I have the odd day where I feel really really happy. It's such a relief, I enjoy the hell out of them. I had a day last week where I pottered around my local neighbourhood and 3 hours in I realised that for the first time in 18 months I wasn't anxious, I didn't have that voice in my head saying 'I hate it here, can we go home now?'. I felt relaxed, walking from shop to shop, enjoying winter sunshine, just doing my thing. Huge progress.

Can you heal yourself?

Heal yourself with the light of the sun and the rays of the moon. With the sound of the river and the waterfall. With the swaying of the sea and the fluttering of birds. Heal yourself with mint, neem, and eucalyptus. Sweeten with lavender, rosemary, and chamomile.

Hug yourself with the cocoa bean and a hint of cinnamon. Put love in tea instead of sugar and drink it looking at the stars. Heal yourself with the kisses that the wind gives you and the hugs of the rain.

Stand strong with your bare feet on the ground and with everything that comes from it. Be smarter every day by listening to your intuition, looking at the world with your forehead. Jump, dance, sing, so that you live happier.

Heal yourself, with beautiful love, and always remember
… you are the medicine.

~ María Sabina, healer and poet.

I've always believed intellectually that we have the power to heal ourselves, and there are many many teachers out there who talk about the idea that the human body knows how to heal itself. And then there's the placebo effect which is not disputed at all by doctors – and what is this if it's not using the ability of the mind to heal ourselves?

I see people who claim they healed themselves from cancer without treatment, or that they confounded doctors who gave them a terminal prognosis and they're still alive 20 years later. And I wonder if they're making it up or if they really did it?

Now it's real, it's not an intellectual exercise.

Do I have the power to heal myself? And if so how do I do it? Is it as simple as just believing that you can? Or do you need to decide that you will? Decide feels more definitive, less room for doubt.

I'm experimenting in meditation with bringing light into my body and using it to illuminate my central nervous system and every cell in my body.

I refuse to stop driving

I can't allow this to stop me from driving forever. It makes me feel helpless. And I feel embarrassed to tell people. I decide to break it down into achievable chunks.

Earlier this week I got on my scooter and went half a mile down the road and came back – bit pathetic really but it is what it is.

Today I make it a couple of miles to the edge of the CBD and back. I can't say I wasn't nervous – there was an anxiety attack waiting to happen, but I was able to manage it.

I hung out there for a while, and allow my central nervous system to acclimitase to being out the house. Good job me. Next time I'll go further.

'You look well!'

For large parts of the time I didn't look much different to my usual self or to anyone else. I definitely didn't look like I had a life-threatening illness.

This didn't help me at all – the cognitive dissonance I had was extreme. I would look in the mirror and see a well person staring back at me, which made it really hard to accept that I had cancer. It made it hard too, to accept that I needed to slow down, that I couldn't be my usual self, that I had to say no to friends, and in the end that I had to spend literally months sleeping. In retrospect I wish I'd slowed down sooner – the body needs all that energy for healing – and that's going on in the inside where you can't see it.

It made dealing with people very challenging too: them treating me as if there's nothing wrong or different wore thin. They don't realise how utterly exhausted you feel. Out of kindness, they want to do things like take you out for dinner. And inside you're thinking all I want to do is stay home and die. People will talk at you the same way they always do and your central nervous system will be begging for them to just slow down, to speak more quietly, to just stop talking please I can't stand it anymore – it feels like violence on your system, and your brain is mush after everything you've just been through and you can't process information that's complex or delivered too quickly.

After my surgeries, I was so exhausted I couldn't even understand words or sentences that were being spoken to me. After chemo it was even worse – my memory went and I couldn't finish sentences.

And because you look so 'well' (the word I keep hearing) they think you don't need help any more. They have busy lives too.

Once you're starting to get through the worst, there's this expectation that you'll go back to normal. All I could manage was sitting there like a stunned mullet trying to work out WTF just happened. I felt some judgement about this. Not sure if it was in my head or if it was real, but I felt an expectation of being normal, and when I kept pointing out that I was far from normal I felt like a negative nelly. It felt that the expectation was that I should be well by now, I should want to leave the house and go places. All I want to do is sleep. I have no desire to be anywhere other than at home and in bed.

Now my hair is growing back it's become even more annoying. People say to me you look so well. And I know they're being kind – they're trying to express that I look better than I did 6 months ago when I had no hair and no colour in my skin. And honestly now I'm realising that you can look well but be very very ill with cancer, I resent the 'you look well' comments. I could be looking as well as this and still have cancer. Looking well doesn't mean for one second that it isn't hiding in my body ready to make a comeback.

Hypochondria!

Before cancer I was whatever the opposite of a hypochondriac is (can't find a word on Google). I hate doctors and only ever visit when something serious is wrong. I tend to power through when I shouldn't – I'm that person who would have to have their leg hanging off before I would think about going to hospital. I tend to think most things sort themselves out.

But now!

I think every minor change in my body is the cancer making a comeback. Even though I try not to focus on it, it's there, in my consciousness.

I feel a new mole on my leg. I'm convinced I have skin cancer and I'm going to die.

Every time I feel a bit tired or dizzy the thought crosses my mind – the cancer is back and it's in my brain and I'm going to die. Should I call the oncologist tomorrow and ask for an MRI?

I have a sore throat the same week that our lockdown is extended and I have actual anxiety attacks – I have convinced myself that my immune system is weak and covid has got me and I'm going to either die alone in this house or intubated in a hospital. Either way I'm alone as I die. After months of not needing valium I give in.

One night I see a lump on my leg. I get an anxiety attack and become convinced it's stage 4 cancer and I'm going to die. I take a valium and put myself to sleep.

I go to see my oncologist about a lump in my solar plexus (the bit in-between the ribs). The problem with the breast area is that there are lumps there all the time and it's easy to convince yourself that a lump isn't normal.

I can't remember if it's always been there or if it's a new arrival. Apparently it's a piece of cartilage called the Xiphoid Process. Who knew?

I'm really conscious that my anti-hypochondria got me into this mess in the first place – if I'd gone to see about my lump sooner things might have been easier. I don't want to make the same mistake again. But equally I don't want to be a pain in the arse for my oncologist. I could literally be there every week getting something or other checked.

I suppose in time this will get easier.

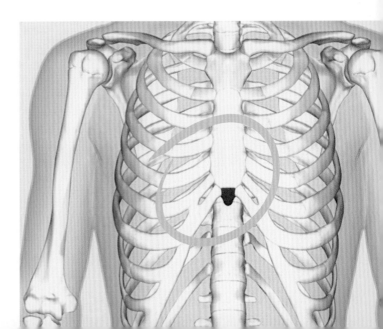

God is in the small things

This phrase keeps coming to mind.

I used to live my life aiming high and shooting for the big things. I was the go big or go home type, always reaching for the stars, no matter how much it cost me.

I'm not so sure now. I'm more drawn now to the simple things. Being with my dogs, having a no-stress day, a good night's sleep, gardening. I think in missing the small things, I've missed so much living.

Please don't call me a breast cancer survivor – or a warrior

How do I talk about myself now? I don't like the idea of being a breast cancer survivor at all. It jars.

Who knows if I've survived yet? All I've survived so far is the treatment. The cancer itself could come back. It feels premature, popping the champagne corks too early for me – let's not tempt fate.

The survivor word has connotations of victory too, and I don't feel victorious. There's nothing in particular I did that makes me a survivor, I just got lucky. It feels like a thing that happened. I don't need any dramatic verbiage or nomenclature, I just did what I had to do, I did what anyone would do. People survive far worse than this every day.

But mostly, it feels judgemental to me – as if the ones who didn't make it failed in some way. Cancer is more random than that. Good people, good women, die of cancer all the time. There's no failure in death.

I feel connected in an imperceptible way to all the women who didn't make it. I feel their struggle, how much they would have wanted to live, how much they would have tried. I think of them, sick and ill and tired and hairless as I was, doing everything it takes to survive this life, and then having to give it up – how much bravery and grace they must have had to summon to do it. I know now, how hard that would be. We are united in a common experience that only we understand.

Am I a breast cancer warrior then? That doesn't work either really. I definitely was not brave enough to give myself that one.

I'm going to stick with "I just did breast cancer" I think.

July

Although I sense my health is generally improving, I feel really lost this week.

Old life is gone, zero chance of going back. Zero. But new life not yet visible. And too tired to bring it to life.

All I'm sure of is that I can't go back to who I was and how I lived before. I suppose at least that gives me something to anchor on – there's no going back.

I feel completely cut off from my past – none of it makes sense or appears to mean anything. I wonder what I have been doing – who was that person? We're used to life being a continuum – one thing leads to another to another, and to there being some logical connection between them. This is not that. There is an abruptness – a distinct before and after, and the only connection between them is that it's me who is experiencing them. I feel that I'm starting again, not sure if I'm to bring anything with me, or if it's even possible to bring anything across this chasm. And maybe that's the point.

In a way treatment was easier than this nowhere place. There was a singular focus and a specific objective – make it through the treatment, make the cancer go away. This phase is harder in some ways: exhaustion, not knowing what to do, the constant fear that every ache and pain is stage 4 cancer and that I'll be dead soon. How do you face this enemy?

There's a weird conundrum in that I can't deal with a lot of human interaction, but I would really like more of it. The problem seems to be that small talk feels pointless to me at the moment, and the large stuff I really want to talk about is a bit too deep for most people. Plus I've used up all my chips with my friends. Who wants to hear their boring cancer friend going on after all this time? I pretend I'm fine. And then I get angry that I'm pretending. Am I angry at me, or them?

LOTS of people say to me "you look well" which of course is well meaning, and it's meant to convey that I look less like shit than I have at any point in the last year. It's driving me nuts. I hear all the time about people who looked 'well' all the way up to the moment they died. In some illnesses you look ill, but with cancer you can look fine. A great friend said it to me the other day and then she apologised: "sorry babe, don't know why I said that, my mum looked fine almost to the end" (her mum died).

I have delayed onset of rage. I didn't feel hugely angry before this. Today, right now, I could scream. It's a very visceral thing – it's in my body not my head. I feel it at night when I try to sleep. I could smash things. I have no idea what I'm angry at. Or if it's even anger. It could be just a release of pent up stuff.

This week I googled 'brain damage from chemo' – again. It was from desperation that my brain still doesn't function the way it used to. I have a permanent ringing in my head, I'm dizzy, my sense of balance is off, and there's a general confusion and discombobulation.

I do have the odd day where I feel optimistic and breezy – those happy for no reason days – and I make plans for the future. But then for days after that I'm back to feeling flat again, exhausted after doing the breakfast dishes, convinced that every weirdness in my body is the cancer coming back, and totally lacking a connection to any sense of purpose about my life. What's the point?

My mind is turning to money. The idea of going back to work just to earn money depresses me. How will I find the energy? How will I find the motivation? It seems so utterly futile when I know there's a countdown clock marking the days to the finish line. Why would I spend any of those days in an office with people I don't know doing work to make money for other people? It just doesn't make sense to me any more. I'm meeting a financial advisor to review what I've managed to accumulate over the years to see whether I've done enough to buy myself freedom.

I met a woman this week who said to me she was depressed for about 2 years after her cancer. I wouldn't categorise my experience as depression, more a combo of existential nothingness and exhaustion, but I can see how it would manifest as depression quite easily. This morning I'm up early to train powerlifting. I've entered Nationals this year, as I always do. I'm even hoping to break one of my own records. It's the only thing I'm making myself do. Some days the hunger to train (and win) is there, some days – today – I just want to lie in bed all day and eat ice-cream. But my sense is that sometimes, even though we don't feel like it, it's best to maintain a thread of connection to the world, and to do our best to keep this alive while we wait for the other things to come back online. Or not.

I know I trust my body. Maybe time and more sleep is all that's required. And patience and kindness to self. I know that what can be recovered will be recovered. What that will look like, I have no idea.

I've started to lose my connection to some of the awe. It's so hard to sustain that level of consciousness – but I must, otherwise what was the point? I have to remind myself sometimes now – this day will never come again, enjoy it, whatever it brings, love it like you chose it Jane. Just keep saying yes to life.

I can feel myself start to get a bit restless, which is usually how I feel when change is coming. It means there's something going on in there! I know there'll come a natural conclusion to this sitting around doing not much and that I'll know when it's time to do something again. But not quite ready yet. Almost.

I still can't believe I had cancer

I still don't believe that I had cancer, it doesn't feel like it could possibly have happened to me. It just doesn't make sense. I wonder if I'll ever feel that it happened to me. I'm a person who eats well and goes to the gym and meditates. And no-one in my family has cancer. I just can't compute.

I have to be really really honest with myself: illness doesn't compute with the idea of myself as a 'successful' alpha female. It's a challenge to my human sense of what I am. Cancer/illness is weakness, no? I do not see myself that way. There's something in here that I don't understand yet.

I say it out loud a lot to friends – "I had cancer" – because I'm trying to force it to be real for myself. I need it to be real, not distant. I want to be able to own this part of my life because it feels important for it be mine. And I can't yet.

As I've been going through my photos and diary notes for this book a large part of the experience is a blank. Maybe the chemo has something to do with this, but I suspect it's also the brain protecting itself from the trauma of the thing. It's how we process shock right?

How do I stop this thing from coming back?

I've become a full-time cancer researcher now.

What causes cancer? How do you stop cancer coming back? I need to know. It's frustrating. From what I can gather there's no definitive answer to either of those questions (unless you're in the 5% or so of women who have a genetic cancer).

But it seems to boil down to:

- Loving your life: having an abundance of love and joy and friendships

- The right amount of stress but not too much

- Good sleep

- My oncologist says 'eat the Mediterranean diet' but I've seen others who say that all animal proteins lead to cancer and so best to eat vegan/raw. What everyone seems to agree on is eating loads of fruit and veg – I've read 10-15 portions a day – cutting out sugar and processed food, eating things that help the gut

- Exercising/moving every day, not carrying too much fat/weight

- Not smoking or drinking

- Reducing toxins from your environment.

- I've read a lot about soy, mushrooms, aspirin, cannabis and vitamin D

Which means, all the things we know we're meant to do now become matters of actual life and death, not theoretical, but very real.

The more I read about the data and the science the more I'm developing a theory that a lot of our modern illnesses are because we're simply not made for the life we're living. We're beings of nature, meant to be outdoors, breathing fresh air and absorbing sunshine on our skin, eating unprocessed food free of toxins, and not spending our lives stressing about work/mortgages/money. Is cancer the price we're paying for our modern lives?

The good news is that I'm doing everything right. I would get 10/10 for post-cancer recuperation, ever the over-achiever. The reality check however is that I've been doing all that healthy living for a long time, which means there's another reason I got cancer and I don't know what it is.

The gravity of my situation is really landing now. I used to say to myself and to others 'there's no returning to normal after this', but I didn't appreciate quite how much change it was going to bring. This is serious. Making a big change is now non-negotiable. I've wanted to make changes for a long time. If not now, when? The way I've been living – is not it.

THERE IS NO TIME TO WASTE

I thought I'd made my peace with the death thing. But at this time a close friend dies and I cry for days – it's not just crying, it's sobbing, it's heartbreak. Someone I've never met but who I follow on Instagram dies. I cry and feel sad for a week. A friend of a friend dies. The adopted mum of my best friend dies.

Of course I'm crying for them, but I'm crying for me too. It's the reminder that death can just come and take you. You can be here – and then you are gone. Both of these women were vital – strong, very much enjoying their life – they weren't ill or frail. Even after so much contemplation on the nature of life and death it still shocks me – that like these women one day I will be gone too, and how little say in it I have.

I feel that death is stalking me. But I don't know if that's true, or if it's simply that we notice things once our attention is drawn to them. I'm sure death has always been there, I just never paid it any attention before.

It was so much easier to be ok with the idea of my own death when I was in the midst of treatment – when I was being hammered by the chemo, I didn't have the wherewithal to resist. Now I feel more well there are so many things I want to do before that time comes.

We're still in lockdown here after a year and a half, and I'm unable to do any of those things. My time here is ticking away. What if I don't get a chance to 'do' any of these things? How do I be at peace anyway?

I'm pondering the concept of the eternal and infinite soul, the idea that there is a bit of us that never 'dies', that it's just our body that is finite. There's a lot of comfort in this. Not to mention excitement. What if this thing that we've been told is the end is in fact the beginning of something wonderful?

I'll probably never know the answer to that question, and so I come back to there is only now.

There is no time to waste. Why is it so hard for us to own our dreams and to run towards them? What stops us from living exactly the life we want to live? Why do we not even know the life we want to live?

244

I am forever changed

In meditation today I see a phoenix in a burst of red and I hear 'let it all go and start again'. I know beyond all doubt that I am changed forever. My old life is never coming back. Sometimes that's thrilling and I can lean into it. Other times the idea of having to get out there and make a new one is just exhausting.

I feel ok today

I have a feeling today of being just really really happy to be alive. It's the first time in almost 2 years that I woke up and didn't feel all kinds of awful in my body. I have an inkling, a vague reminder, of what it feels like to be me again. Peaceful. Cheerful.

I have the sense of feeling more free than I've ever felt: it's as if the cancer has wiped the slate clean. There is no past, no memories, no looking back, nothing weighing me down. I'm free of other people's expectations, free to say what I think without reservation, free to be me, free to move forward, free to do whatever I want.

And my hair is cute for the first time too.

Letting go of powerlifting

I should have been competing today in Nationals. I've been training for months and was ready to break some Australian records: my biggest comp lifts since before cancer 2 years ago. With the wind behind me I might have been on for a 155KG deadlift.

It's cancelled: it's 2021 so of course it is. I know it's not important in the scheme of things, but I'm devastated – it was the last/only bit of normal that I've held onto through this whole thing and it's gone. I've been miserable for days.

I feel a strong need to let go of all my old normal – even powerlifting. I need to stop trying. It feels like struggle. I need to allow everything to be as it is. It feels better, easier, more peaceful. And honestly, my whole body hurts. Where they cut into my breast and my armpit is a mess – everything is stuck onto my rib cage and my whole torso is twisted. It's time for some rehab rather than heavy weights.

I've been really unsettled and tearful this week. There's so much tension in the air – the Sydney lockdown, the never-ending lockdown in Melbourne. It's been almost 18 months, and it looks like it'll be another 6 months at least. It's feeling harder than ever before. I'm lonely, I'm bored. I want to have some fun now. I think I made it through cancer but I haven't made it through covid yet.

I re-read what I wrote last year – everything is ending. It feels that this was a premonition.

It's the first time that I've felt down, demoralised, dispirited, hopeless. I can't be bothered to do anything. Even small things feel annoying and impossible.

If times were different I'd be doing the post-cancer thing – traveling the world and being with friends and having fun. Instead I'm stuck at home. What if I only have a few years left and I look back and I've spent most of it locked down at home? In the absence of being able to do what I want, what do I do? How do I make my life mean something?

I just saved my life

I just today understood that cancer treatment is the act of saving our own life. What I mean is, if we do nothing, there is only one conclusion – our own demise. And so the act of undertaking treatment is therefore the act of saving our life.

I don't know why I didn't understand this before. I think back to my diagnosis and treatment and how I handled it – as if it was just another thing on my to do list, another project among my many projects, something to be squeezed in among work and training and all my other things. An inconvenience.

This explains the later feelings of shock and the enormity of the grief. My subconscious knew this was serious.

Maybe this is how we protect ourselves from the fear? By carrying on as normal and pretending it's not a matter of life and death?

Had I known this, would I have made different decisions? Maybe. Although I'm not sure I could have afforded to.

It seems utterly inhumane to me that we're forced to work and to keep going, when faced with cancer. Most of us have worked or contributed to society for years before we get ill. Why is there no financial support to enable us to take time out to focus just on healing?

I'm feeling more and more a sense of self-respect: at what I did, what I was able to do. I just saved my life.

Made with love

As I've been tidying the house after a crazy 18 months I find these – bags that I was given to carry my drainage bottle around after surgery to remove my lymph nodes.

At the time I was so lost in my own story and fear I didn't appreciate at all the kindness of this gesture. Now I look at them and feel the love that went into making these little bags: a woman I've never met made them by hand for a woman she would never meet. I feel singularly ungrateful that I didn't appreciate them before.

Huge shoutout to the Zonta women in Melbourne who do this.

THE END

My lucky socks — can't
bear to throw them away

I wanted this book to end neatly -
a happy ending. It isn't to be like
that. I don't know where this story
ends or even what happens next.
Another spring has come and gone
and it's 2 years since this thing
started, 2 years since I felt 'good'.
I can count on one hand the number
of days that I've woken up and felt
well - or even just like me. I feel off
somehow, I don't have a groove any
more, what a friend calls 'your own
unique note in the universe'. At the
time of writing, the world's longest
lockdown continues, which means 2
years of being essentially alone.
My body is weak. Reading my
diaries, I think I've been experiencing
a depression the last few months,
a crash. It makes sense that this
would happen. I try to stay optimistic,
to believe that I can rebuild my life,

but it may be that the question now is how to live with a body that is never fully well again.

There is a before and after Jane. I don't even recognise who I was before — it feels like a distinct + definite break. I look at my old self and my old life with curiosity. Was that really me? The amount of change, loss and grief I'm processing feels like vertigo. Nothing makes sense any more, my words sound like noise. How do we find meaning once we've realised that nothing actually matters?

It's not just cancer, it's menopause, it's covid, it's what's happening in the world. We've being forced into a new era, and there's no way back.

My inner voice says "You've crossed a bridge Jane, don't look back, there's nothing there." I feel a need to mark the end of this somehow. It feels unfinished. I think a tattoo is coming.

My morning meditation has been the same for months — THANKFULNESS

It's not the same as gratitude I've realised, which tends to be dependent on 'good' things happening that day, things I liked or wanted. It's deeper. It's thankfulness for this day, no matter what. Even inside of all my grief and loss and hardship, the inconvenience of illness, the massive changes in my life, I can still look to the cosmos and be in devotion to the mystery. Choosing to love life to live fully, in the face of everything is my only choice, or else what was it all for?
I used to think that having meaning meant trying to change the world, now I think it's more about appreciating the simple fact of our extraordinary existence.
And love. Always Love.

X

MUS

INGS

After a cancer diagnosis

There is no one way or perfect way to do cancer: do what you need to do. And remember: just doing your best every day is a victory.

Medical considerations

Ask how much time you have before treatment needs to start, and consider whether you want to move quickly or take time if you have it.

Do you want to get a cancer coach who can help you to interpret your results, scans, blood tests and help you make decisions?

Do you have the medical team you want, or do you want a second opinion or to change doctors?

Do you want to research/explore your treatment options? (There may or may not be options.)

Do you want to research treatments you can do in parallel with medical procedures to alleviate side-effects, improve their efficacy, and help you recover afterwards?

Do you want to speak to other women about their experiences, as input into your own decision-making process?

Are you going to trust your medical team or do you want to research and know about breast cancer and the various treatments?

How much do you want to know about your prognosis?

The emotional reaction

Have a way of processing your emotions: specifically, have strategies for managing fear/stress/anxiety because these things adversely affect your body's ability to heal.

Do you want support from someone outside of your friends/family circle (therapist, coach, support group)?

Telling people/dealing with people

Get close the friends you can depend on to be unemotional and non-judgemental in their emotional support.

How are you going to tell people/ manage social media? Decide how you're going to own the narrative, be clear about how you want this to be received and whether you want opinions/advice or not.

Be aware of the fear and opinions of others: reduce your interactions with anyone who doesn't make you feel good, and start protecting yourself energetically. Imagine yourself as a bubble of energy, any colour you like, and make the boundary impenetrable. Nothing is allowed through this boundary unless you choose it.

Practical planning

Be aware that this thing may run for some time and plan accordingly.

What needs to happen in your life so that self-care is your main priority?

Do you want to carry on as normal (e.g. working) or do you want to take time out to focus on your health?

If you work, how are you going to let your place of work know? How much sick leave can you take? Who is it safe to share the news with? How will you protect your position, if you work in a particularly competitive organisation? How will you sustain your business if you're an entrepreneur?

Mobilise the friends who will help with food/kids/pets/house. Tell them exactly what you need - make a list, make an online calendar and ask people to put their names in. Allow them to pay for services if they don't have time.

Who will do hospital/specialist visits with you? Brief them on what you need: note-taking, question-asking, emotional support.

Outsource if you can afford it: cleaners, dog-walkers, child-minders, meal delivery services.

What do you need to make hospital visits bearable?

Do you like being in your home/bedroom? You'll likely be spending a lot of time there, so make it a place you enjoy being.

Make a will and legal/medical power of attorney. It helps to settle your mind that this has been done.

Get your finances in order. If you go private there are costs - ask how much it's going to be. If there is an impact on your earnings - work this out.

Healing and life changes

On a mental/emotional/spiritual level ask yourself what needs to heal and be honest with yourself. This is a powerful moment to tune in.

Evaluate your nutrition, exercise, stress, how much water you drink, alcohol consumption, smoking.

Your Heroine's Journey

Mark the start of the journey somehow - it could be as simple as lighting a candle and sitting with yourself for a while or going for a long walk. Think about getting into nature. Make a commitment to yourself and your healing, to being open to wherever this thing takes you.

Buy a journal and start writing down whatever comes through each day. Everything that's about to happen to you is forming a new story of your life - be really alive to it, and how you're changing.

Ask yourself who you want to be throughout this. Decide the story that's going to get you through and write it down to remind yourself on the days that it's hard.

What soothes your soul? Prioritise it. Is there something meaningful or beautiful that you might create during this time?

257

Dealing with the medical system

No-one tells you what to expect when you get cancer. There's no brochure, or video, or talk from anyone that tells you what to expect. You're left having to work it out for yourself, or by asking others.

You're not in control and nothing is certain

My experience has been that all the people who were involved in my care were wonderful. (I know this isn't a universal experience.) That said, doing cancer and dealing with the medical system is incredibly frustrating if you're a woman who likes to have definitive answers to questions, or you like to make/have plans, or you're used to having control.

Joining the dots

Everyone in the process is deeply specialised and there isn't anyone who pulls it all together for you: you have to do this for yourself, as a non-expert, while you're in shock, and often while you're tired. Each expert in the process wants to do a consult with you, get their own bloodwork done, and has their own unique lens on your case. If you work in an environment where you're used to having every possible future scenario mapped out, with probabilities, and pros and cons - this is going to be a big

surprise. In cancer you get none of this.

Time

I found that being ill is almost a full-time job: for almost a year there was hardly a week when I wasn't doing blood tests or medical appointments or recovering from medical appointments – as well as working.

The asymmetry of power and information

If you consider yourself an intelligent woman who's used to making her own decisions about things be prepared for a shock. Medical processes are not designed around you, and you're likely to feel disempowered, frustrated, angry, and fearful. You'll be in hospital doing tests not knowing why. You'll be taking advice without having any expertise or context. Yes you can google or ask for second opinions – but who's to say the information you find online is any better than what comes from your oncologist or your surgeon? And when you're tired you don't have the energy to discern what's good from what's bad. There are services out there that help with this if you want it.

Do you want to know the whole story?

I can't prove this, it's more of a feeling – that doctors, surgeons, oncologists, only tell you what they think you can handle. You might sometimes feel that you're not being told the whole story. Decide how much you want to know, and if you want to know everything make it clear to your entire medical team. Keep asking "is there anything you're not telling me?"

There are always surprises

You don't know what's going to appear next. Things will happen that you weren't warned about or prepared for – they just crop up out of blue. It can feel like a series of trapdoors. Expect and plan for this. And there are financial surprises too: In Australia for instance private medical insurance doesn't cover all medical costs.

Take friends with you to medical appointments

You'll be in shock and you'll be tired. You may experience feeling surprisingly submissive in the face of an expert in a white coat. Bring friends who take notes, ask questions if you freeze, and who remember the things you'll forget because you're in overwhelm.

Healing

Advice on diet, 'alternative' therapies, how to stop the cancer coming back, and how to repair your immune system after the chemo/radio isn't part of the standard service. You'll have to go and find this for yourself.

Medical experts are often the worst people to advise on things like recovery times and questions like 'how quickly can I go back to work, or start exercising?'. Trust your own instinct.

And don't forget – medicine can cut out the cancer or reduce the tumour, but the deep healing has to be done by you.

Your Options

1) Pay someone to help you join the dots.

2) Spend time doing it yourself. Become conversant with what's happening, ask lots of questions, do research, speak to other women.

3) Trust the medical advice and roll with it.

Fear

It's impossible to escape fear when you have cancer. You're not failing when it happens. And you're not weak. Fear is simply your mind trying to protect you – it's warning you of danger and the unknown. The thing is not to demonise it. What if your fear was an entirely rational response to the situation you find yourself in?

Cancer = Death

The idea that Cancer = Death is in our collective consciousness. Even though they go to great lengths to reassure you that breast cancer is a "good cancer" the fear programme is likely to be triggered immediately.

The shock of our own death

We all live as if death isn't going to happen to us, but cancer reminds you that it definitely is. Maybe not now, but at some point. Many of us have never thought about or prepared for our own death, and now we cannot avoid the idea of it. The emotional reaction to this is deep and primal. It's part shock at the sudden realisation of how fragile we all are, how tenuous our connection to life is, and how easily all of this can simply be over; Part a realisation of our own irrelevance, that life will go on without us eventually, which is a huge challenge to our human ego; And part grief – I don't want to die yet, I'm not ready to leave. There's often fear of the actual process of death too – will I be in pain? It's a lot to process.

Hospitals/dealing with the medical system

Even though many of the people who work in cancer care are wonderful and deeply caring, the system is designed to get a job done, it's not designed around patient comfort. There are terrifying machines. There's an almost total lack of control or knowledge. There's surprise after surprise on the journey, which means we never quite know what's coming next. And the treatments aren't an awful lot of fun. There's a lot to be fearful of.

Why fear is not helpful to you

Fear materially impacts the immune system: it turns it off. And you need your immune system firing on all cylinders when you have cancer.

What to do when the fear comes

Unless you're a Zen monk, fear is going to come. You need strategies for dealing with it when it does.

Summon your superpowers: It might feel counterintuitive, but it's easier to access our superpowers in times of great fear or adversity. At our lowest ebb we're forced to reach for something beyond the ordinary, and when we do we realise we have boundless courage inside of us. It doesn't mean you don't feel fear but it doesn't paralyse you – you have the ability to keep going. Be confident that there is a part of you that is as tough as steel and it will not let you down. You can depend on yourself entirely. You realise that safety does not come from the world outside of you, it's in you, and when you know this you can handle anything.

Allow it: We don't like uncomfortable emotions like fear or anxiety, they're considered to be negative emotions. But all emotions have an evolutionary reason to exist – the role of fear is to bring your attention to danger and help you to survive. It's not your enemy, it's here to help you. Rather than fight it, can you allow it? Can you welcome it in? It's often more helpful to admit 'I'm absolutely fucking terrified today' than to pretend it's not there. Can you thank it for trying to protect you?

Talk to your fear: "I see you fear, but you're not running the show today."

You are not your fear: Say to yourself 'I am feeling fear'. This reminds you that you are not the fear, the fear is not all of you. The fear is a temporary visitor, it comes and it goes – it is not you.

Mindset: What's the story you're running and is it working for you? How optimistic are you? When we can find some meaning in our suffering it helps us to deal with fear and pain.

Is there something I need to know? Interrogate it. Ask if there's something important the fear is trying to convey. Perhaps the fear is a genuine messenger – maybe you don't feel right about something. It could be your intuition talking. Always trust your gut. Ask if there's something you need to know.

Why am I scared? Try the 5 Whys: ask "Why am I scared?" And ask 5 times. Sometimes you find you're not scared at all, or you're not scared of the thing you thought you were scared of.

Learn to soothe yourself: Talk to yourself out loud, soothe yourself the way you would a friend or a child: "You're doing great, you've got this, you've done bigger things than this before." Hold yourself with all the love you can muster.

Is this mine? All emotions are connected to a story that we're running. In the moment, ask yourself "is this my story?" You might find it's someone else's story, or a story that belongs to the collective. If it's not yours, let it go. Simply say to yourself "this is not my story". That's the end of it. Protect yourself from other people's fear by putting an impenetrable ring around yourself - nothing gets in unless you say it does. Your job is simply to protect the boundary at all times.

Essential oils: I carried my favourite oils all the time: Sandalwood for relaxation, White Angelica for hospitals to overpower the smell. Pick oils that you like and that help you to relax.

Body hacks: Try CBD oil, reishi mushroom tea, valium when all else fails. Get all your vitamins and minerals tested: if you're low on essentials like iron, B12, vitamin D your body will often let you know this by manifesting fear or anxiety.

Breathing/meditation: Breathwork and meditation are really helpful tools for self–managing your central nervous system. Go and lie on the ground – preferably on the earth or the grass – and allow it to slow down your nervous system. Allow all your fear to float away into the wind, to melt into the earth.

Move it through: All emotions should come and go – they're temporary. So, move the fear when it arrives to avoid it getting stuck. Walking, dancing, jumping up and down, banging the chest, shouting, singing loudly, pulling the hair on your head. Whatever works to make sure it passes through instead of hanging around. SCREAM if you need to. It's very therapeutic.

Surround yourself with love: Love is the answer! The human heart plugs into other hearts in ways that we don't really understand. So, get your people and hug them tight. Feel the love and allow it to infuse your body. And by the way giving and feeling love is just as healing. So tell your people you love them all the time. Love your dog. Love yourself. Love your life. As far as you are able do things you love. Surround yourself with beauty. Fill your life with so much love that when the fear comes there isn't enough room for it to set up shop.

Surrender/acceptance: What we're all seeking is solid ground, a guaranteed outcome, someone telling you "it's going to be fine!". In cancer this cannot be guaranteed, and when we feel unsafe, there is fear. As this road has so many twists and turns anchoring ourselves on events – good news or bad news – can be exhausting and demoralising. If we can accept that there is a power greater than ourselves that we cannot control (it's called Life) and that there is no such thing as safety, we're free of needing guarantees. When life is overwhelming all there is for us to do is bow to it – let all our resistance go and submit to what is. In this acceptance, there is not just less fear – there is total liberation. Surrender sounds weak, but it's quite the opposite. It takes immense courage and wisdom to be humble enough to say you know what, this is bigger than me, and I accept it, with grace.

Being ok with death: When we explore our own fear we realise that so much of it is connected to an existential fear of the end. If we can be at peace with this, our day to day fear is put into perspective. We can accept and move more easily with this thing, and handle the hardships along the way. Even if you have a 'good' prognosis I highly recommend that you sit with the idea of your own death and ask yourself what needs to happen for you to be ok with that.

Connect to the divine: I don't fully understand how it works – but I know that even in the midst of fear there is also a divinity, that which is untouched by the drama of the human realm. I know that if I go beyond the fear and ask to know divine grace I feel better. And that if you ask your support team on the other side for help they will help. Don't ask me who they are, I don't know. But I know they will help.

Take solace in your Heroine's Journey: Fear usually means you're on your edge. This is when you start the journey of finding out what you're made of, and who and what you really are. Yes this is hard, and at times you will feel utterly defeated, but at the same time you will be rewarded with a deepening understanding of yourself and of life. You will. There's comfort in that.

About work

Reasons to keep working

It provides structure at a time when everything else is chaotic; It's often a place we get to feel competent which feels good; Income – often we have no choice but to work; Perhaps we work in competitive environments and we want to protect our careers; It's a way of forgetting cancer, which can be overwhelming.

On the other hand

Your body doesn't need stress when she's fighting cancer and processing treatment; And it's utterly exhausting doing treatment and working at the same time, especially if you have family to take care of too.

If I was independently wealthy or had a partner with money would I do it again? Absolutely not. If I could stop working now and just focus on my health I would. I want to be alive in 10 years and I'm not sure that work and all the stress that goes with it is worth it to me anymore. After decades of being entirely focussed on my career, my health is now worth more to me. It seems absurd and inhumane to me now that our society is so concerned with staying productive and our lives cost so much that we can't even take time off to be ill.

Taking leave

Check out how much sick leave you can take, how much holiday you have, and if you can take unpaid leave.

Whether/how to tell people

I know of a friend of a friend who had decided not to tell anyone. I honestly don't know how you would manage to keep it hidden, but it must have felt important to her to do it this way – not all workplaces feel safe. Consider who you're going to tell and how you're going to own the narrative. Let people know how you want to be treated. Have an honest conversation with the person who has an influence on your performance ratings, salary, and promotions, to ensure you're adequately protected.

Be prepared for the possibility that this thing might be bigger than you realise

Be realistic. You'll be at the doctors and hospitals regularly, and it all takes a lot of time out of a working week. You may bounce back really quickly, but on the other hand your treatment and recovery may run for years. It may take time before you feel 100%. You may never be back at 100%.

Be prepared for the fact that emotionally this is going to take a toll on you. Even if you're a strong, resilient woman this thing is an extraordinary emotional rollercoaster and it's going to affect your productivity and capacity. Make plans to either reduce your load, or to bolster the team around you to step up and deliver.

Get clear on priorities for how you use your limited energy

Get crystal clear on what matters and what doesn't, gracefully let go of what's not important, hand it over to someone else, or put it on the backburner. Agree this with the relevant people at work, so it doesn't reflect badly.

Make your health your biggest priority

Don't feel guilty if you're not pulling your weight for a while, and don't overwork when you're exhausted to prove a point. It's not worth it. Over the duration of our careers we all have moments when we contribute more and less. A good workplace understands give and take. You've paid your dues and this is a time for you to focus on yourself. Your health matters more for a while.

Managing stress at work

If your job involves lots of stress, what can you do about this? What routines can you build into your day/week to destress if you feel it build up? What can you do so that you're not doing long days? How can you take stress-inducing work off your to do list – are there others who can help you? Meditate, and breathe, for stress reduction whenever you need it.

Have a plan for maximising your health and energy

Prioritise good sleep, good food, and movement/exercise to support your body. Give her all the help you can. Get help if you're dealing with cancer or menopausal symptoms like anxiety, depression, brain fog, tiredness, sickness, overheating. There are medical and alternative treatments that can really help. Get all your vitamins and minerals tested by a good doctor and have a plan for food and supplements if you need them – low B vitamins, iron, and vitamin D can all affect your mood and your energy. Get help from a nutritionist, or dietician if you need it and can afford it.

Have a support network at work

There are going to be bad days when you feel awful or you can't perform. Build a support network of people you trust and who will rescue you at 5 minutes' notice if you just can't manage something. Don't be too proud to ask for help.

Friends & other people

When you have cancer, dealing with friends and other people is surprisingly complicated. Here's what I learnt.

There is so much kindness on this road.

Many people will go out of their way to help you.

We really need people

Breast cancer is not a thing to do alone. We need a lot of help, practically and emotionally. We're wired for connection.

You'll lose friends but Human Angels will show up in their place

People you think are on your A team just won't show up. You'll lose some people altogether. Learn to be ok with this. Don't expect anything, don't take it personally. New friends will show up and go above and beyond.

The people you want on your team:

They can stay calm and not drop into their own fear, they'll drive you to (many) medical appointments, they don't mind sitting waiting in hospitals for HOURS, they don't freak when you throw up or cry or are vulnerable, they will attend oncology/specialist appointments to ensure you ask your questions and remember the answers when you go blank, they will help you problem-solve when you're exhausted, they will make food and run errands without needing anything in return, they can sit quietly without needing anything from you, they can listen without needing to say anything or offer opinions, they keep telling you you're doing great, and they unconditionally support you come what may.

Not everyone is suited for this moment

There are people you will need to either protect yourself from or remove from your life: They carry fear or shame about illness, death and bodies (it's infectious); They make you responsible for their emotional reaction to your illness; They have strong opinions about your situation that aren't helpful; They can't let you feel how you feel; They can't cope with deep grief and extreme emotions; They tell you to 'cheer up' or 'stay positive' when you're at the end of your tether instead of just saying 'yep, this is shit'; They're tiring to be around because they can't slow down to your pace, they talk too much, or they're high drama; They tell you about the people in their family who died of cancer; They send emails and links to random ideas about your cancer that confuse you; They want to make plans for the future and you're only just about managing to put one foot in front of the other.

Most people will not understand you and cancer is lonely

Unless you've walked this path you simply cannot understand – even really close friends will often have no idea what you're dealing with. You'll find this frustrating. Sometimes you'll try and explain yourself, other times you'll just give up and walk away because you're too tired. Decide who's worth trying to explain this to, because you want them in your life, and who isn't.

Learn to say no and to prioritise yourself for now

And be ok with that. Your focus is on healing from cancer.

Allowing people to help you is an art form

Say yes to all the help that's offered. Don't be proud. Allow people to love you: love is healing on so many levels. And when they do – show gratitude, be graceful in receiving, make it a pleasure for them to look after you. This is an act of love on their part, so receive it as such. One of the upsides of this experience is all the beautiful moments of genuine human connection you'll experience.

Ask for specific things

This is not a time to be vague and to assume that people will know what you need. Practise asking for exactly what you want. People will either say yes I can do that or no I can't.

Accept there are parts of this that you're meant to do alone

People can help you but no-one can do the emotional and spiritual healing for you. There are parts of this that are yours to do alone.

When the circus has moved on

Unless a person has had a serious illness, they'll think the important stuff is over as soon as you start to look like yourself again or once treatment is over, and default to business as usual. They don't realise the emotional part is as hard as the treatment. Don't be surprised if you have to keep reminding them you have cancer and that you are far from normal.

Don't be surprised if there are times you just can't people.

There's a lot to process, and the body will be exhausted. Sometimes you just have nothing to give or to say, and it's impossible to explain what's going on and all you want is to sit on your own in an empty room. Don't feel obliged to do anything you don't want – your focus must be on your recovery.

Supporting someone with breast cancer

I get asked ALL THE TIME "how do I support someone with breast cancer?"

Truthfully, it's hard. The person with cancer has a lot to process, they're exhausted, fearful, their emotions are all over the place. They have to be selfish for a while, which means it can feel like one-way traffic. Their illness can go on for years. And then this thing changes them and you wonder who they are now. It's not for everyone.

I hope this helps.

Breast cancer is not normal.

By which I mean it is not like losing a job, it's not a minor life inconvenience. It is next level. Don't expect normal service from your person. This changes everything and they will be all over the place. You have to be flexible and roll with the punches.

Be aware of your own shame around women's bodies or breasts.

Lots of people have shame or feel awkward. Just don't be weird about breasts or bodies.

Be constant, steady, and a source of safety in the midst of chaos.

Let them know they've loved and they're not alone – letting someone know they're not alone is priceless. Be solid, dependable, safe, sweet, tender.

Take care of practical things.

This means the person can focus on their treatment. Don't say general things like "let me know if you need anything". Get specific: "do you need a lift to the hospital?" Or just do it: many people, particularly women, are terrible at asking for help – so just change the sheets, clean the house, cook food, buy flowers. They will be very grateful.

Help with medical appointments.

There's tons of medical appointments so offer to be the driver. Hospital visits can be boring, so keep them company and run errands. When they go for results, go with them – make a list of the person's questions and be ready to jump in and ask them if the person freezes from overwhelm. Write EVERYTHING down. If you're going into hospital with this person, put a ring of protection around them – create an unbreachable ring of light around the both of you to stop the crazy hospital energy getting in. Those places are intense.

Know when to keep morale up and when to be real.

There's a time to tell them they're doing great, to lie and say "you look fucking fabulous babe" even when they don't, and to bring the energy they can't manufacture for themselves. And there's a time to be real: when they want to talk about their fear, their grief, their misery. Be the person who doesn't try and cheer them up with fake positivity on the days they don't want to hear it – know when it's ok to say "yeah that's shit" or "I can see why you feel scared". Be able to sit in the hole with them. Give them the space to not have to pretend to be anything they're not. They will love you if they can just be exactly as they are without having to spend energy on pretending.

This is about them.

Suspend your own emotions, particularly fear. Don't offer opinions, don't make it about you, don't expect them to be responsible for your own emotional reactions. Your role is to support them as they work their way through this, to help them navigate this situation the best way they can. Allow the totality of their experience, their grief, the choices they're making, the sense they're making of it.

It's not your job to fix or rescue.

This is their path to walk. Avoid rescuer/hero dynamics – this is about them and supporting them to be as empowered as possible.

Accept you will never truly understand what they're dealing with.

Unless you've done it yourself of course. Cancer is a huge shock – it's often the first time a person has faced their own mortality, and the treatment is brutal. Assume you don't understand, ask questions, and really listen.

Adjust your energy, tone, volume, speed.

Their central nervous system is feeling horrible. So slow down, speak more quietly than normal, be aware they can't process conversation or ideas easily, that they will lose parts of their normal memory functioning. Be quiet, keep it simple, slow, and calm. Don't be offended if your normal chit chat doesn't interest them.

Don't ask them to make plans for the future.

They don't have the mental capacity for it, and they're exhausted. Go day by day.

This is not a reciprocal relationship for a while.

What you offer must be offered unconditionally. Don't expect anything in return – they've got nothing. Get used to it being one way traffic for as long as it takes. That's just how it is for now.

Tee up your own support crew.

There might be grief for you too, the feeling that the person you knew is no longer here. It may trigger issues with your own life. Consider whether you need your own coach/therapist/teacher. If you're doing a lot of the heavy lifting don't forget to take care of your own health, and to have fun. You still have to live. And finally consider whether this can be a moment of growth for you as much as it is for them. What can you learn in this?

Menopause

Why does no-one ever tell us about the menopause?

It's such a huge change in a woman's life and no-one warns you it's coming. I really think someone should have said at some point 'hey, there's going to come a time when you have no idea who you are anymore, you're going to have anxiety every time you leave your house, and your vagina is going to hurt like hell.'

It's almost more debilitating than the cancer. I could find a way to work and train through cancer, even the worst of it. Menopause is feeling harder in many ways – the anxiety, the brain fog. I understand why so many women leave the workforce. If I didn't have the luxury of being able to work from home I'm not sure I'd be able to do what I used to do. The idea of getting on a train to the office and being in an enclosed space with hundreds of people doing 10 hour days of meetings, and a crushing workload – I just couldn't do it now. I couldn't.

I read a great description of menopause a while ago – I can't recall where, so I can't credit it: That when we're young we're drunk on oestrogen and this is what leads us to do reckless things, to flirt and mate, because we feel invincible and bold and sexy. When we're in menopause we're suffering in the same way as a heroin addict – our body is craving the oestrogen that's gone. We're an addict in withdrawal.

Those of us doing cancer who are forced into menopause by endocrine therapy, or whose cancer happens to come at the same time as menopause, have a double whammy to deal with. A double dose of symptoms to manage, and not knowing what is causing what. A double dose of not knowing who we are and having to put ourselves back together again.

And am I the only woman with breast cancer who has HRT envy? The media is suddenly full of women looking amazing and happy and raving about how HRT changed their lives. They have their lives back! They have hot sex and shiny hair! It's great that these women have found a solution but what's mine? I can barely make it through a day and I honestly don't think I'll ever have sex again.

Of course, I'd heard about the hot flushes that everyone talks about and the appalling sleep. But no-one ever said that this leaves you so tired you feel close to madness. Nor did anyone ever mention any of the following:

- Brain fog that feels like a lobotomy
- Exhaustion
- General irritability which sometimes veers into rage
- Anxiety that's so bad I don't like being out the house and I hate driving
- Depression, feeling flat all the time

- Weight gain
- Skin that's so dry you could lather lard on it and it wouldn't make a difference
- Lack of interest in sex; not feeling sexually attractive to others
- A dry and sore vagina that hurts and doesn't want sex at all
- Joint and body pain – all over
- Heart palpitations
- Being clumsy, dropping and breaking things all the time
- Forgetfulness
- Feeling small and fragile
- Not knowing who you are any more

No-one ever said that sometimes you'll feel like you're literally going mad or dealing with early onset dementia.
Or that you'd be grieving the loss of your younger self. I had no idea how significant a transition it would be. How hard the physical symptoms would be. How different I would feel, that even my identity would feel different.

It's not all bad

All of that said, I can feel some other things coming through. It's a rebirth.

I care so much less about the world – what's going on out there, what people think of me. My relationship with myself is really what matters. There's the feeling of finally owning myself, a liberation I looked for my whole life. And now here it is. My theory is that our female hormones make us want to be amenable, attractive, likeable, fuckable, which makes it hard for us to be ok with not being liked. At this point I no longer care. You can like me or not like me. It doesn't matter. I like me.

You start feeling free to speak truth; actually you start breathing fire. There are so many years of self-censoring and self-doubting to make up for. All the years of feeling scared to speak up or to do the things you really want to do, make, create, in case you're judged and dismissed. You also start swearing a lot too. And you don't care whether someone thinks it's a sign of low IQ. It's not.

You start listening to yourself – and you do exactly what you want. It's not that you become totally selfish, but after a lifetime of doing what others want, and often having your needs, wants, and desires sidelined, you're no longer willing to make your needs secondary. You want what you want. You're going to do what you want to do.

I've started to hugely enjoy not needing to be seen as attractive to men and how this allows me to move through the world in a completely different way. When I walk into a room now I'm not wondering if men are looking at me or admiring me or wanting me. My point is not that I don't want sex – I'd love to be married to a good man one day and do all the things – it's the indiscriminate need for sexual approval that is so limiting. When I was young I made some dodgy choices. My sexual desire at my current wonderful age is ignited by a genuine interest in the person, in them having something interesting to say, and in them showing real interest in me. It responds to whether they show care and love for me, and shuts down appropriately when they don't. I'm able to make good choices and can go without, rather than put up with rubbish. And the flip side is that my relationship with men has changed – quite beautifully. I appreciate men now in a way I never did before.

I've never been more creative or productive. I think once you're stripped of the need to be attractive and you're free to speak your mind, you can get on with the business of being you. I'm enjoying the change of focus – where before most of my energy was spent at work, attracting partners, needing to be social, seeking validation – now ALL my energy and focus is on the things I want to do before I die. I have more ideas than I can get out of my head and onto paper. It drives me nuts that I have so many things I want to create and that there aren't enough hours in the day to do them all. It's the most exciting time of my life in many ways. I can imagine a million possibilities, not just for me, but for the whole fucking world. I just see potential everywhere.

There's a clarity: everything is very very clear and very simple. Increasingly I find those work conversations that go around in circles a challenge: everything is so obvious now. Our ability at this age to see systems rather than parts is a superpower – we see cause and effect, and how all the parts fit together.

There's a huge spiritual dimension to this phase that no— one ever talks about.

There's a change in perspective that just comes naturally. There's the excitement at finally meeting yourself – the sense of finally coming home; An ease and a gracefulness that comes from being

a bit more relaxed about life. There's wisdom – we know what's right and what isn't, we can see clearly, we understand ourselves and others. We stop looking down – instead we look up at the cosmos and we instinctively know that there is more to life than achievements or possessions. We become free of the drive of our ego.

And as we realise there's an end to life we stop wasting time on things that don't matter. We want love and peace and good times with good people.

All of which is very similar to the cancer rite of passage. And so, while we're unfortunate in that we get a double dose of the symptoms, we also get a double dose of the upside. We're catapulted forward as new people with superpowers.

Menopause needs a good PR. it's the most powerful time of a woman's life - but no-one ever tells you it's coming, or about all the good shit that's waiting for you on the other side of the hideous symptoms.

And here's an idea that someone should campaign for: we should get paid leave to go off and menopause in peace for a few years if we want to.

Female, femininity & feminism

The breast cancer/menopause combo has been an interesting exploration of my sense of what it means to be female and feminine and a feminist.

I've always been very much the archetypal white Gen X feminist – I worked, earnt my own money, had no kids, was able to take wonderful holidays and invest in myself, could afford to buy my own house and live alone, was beholden to no-one (outside of work). There's a lot to be grateful for and to love about the life I've been able to have. It was a life my mum and her generation weren't able to have and that many of them wanted for their daughters – the freedom, the education, the adventures. I always felt that my mum sacrificed a lot to enable me to have this life and I've always wanted to show her that I took what she gave me and made the most of it.

I've thought a lot this year about all the ways in which I've rejected being female – it's what women in my generation were encouraged to do to make it in our careers. We were told we had to develop a tough work persona. I've also thought about how my feminism – which was just as much about not liking or trusting men than it was about supporting women – made me hard-edged too. In combination these two forces have made me entirely unable to be loved or helped.

The breast cancer has brought on a femininity I've never felt before. There's so much softness trying to find its way to the surface. It's dismantling the protection I've built up against the world. I used to think of softness as weakness; now it feels that life itself is flowing through me.

It's the end for me now, of the corporate-masculine persona that carried me through most of my career. I was already getting tired of her and now we've broken up completely. I like how this feels. It feels overdue. I want to know how it feels to be expressed as a woman now.

As a Gen X feminist who was brought up on the idea that 'women need a man like a fish needs a bicycle', it was also a huge surprise to admit to myself that I would have given anything for a strong masculine presence wrapped around me this year – a protector and provider – so that I could relax into the illness and not have to tough it out. While on one level I feel a huge sense of self-respect for all the ways I've taken care of myself, it isn't right that anyone should do cancer alone. We need to be cared for at such a vulnerable time.

I also felt the absence of a community. Lockdown of course played a part in this, but it was more than just being isolated from people – I realised I'm not woven into other people's lives in a meaningful way. So many people offered me so much, but I'm the archetypal woman who lives alone and who doesn't belong anywhere or to anyone.

It's fine and dandy when life is going well – when your career is doing great, and you have money and health, and the world is your oyster. It is not fun at all when you're alone and very ill. Who would sit with me if I was dying? You're nobody's number one person. These are important questions as our generation ages: how we can better support each other and live in some kind of community?

I burnt out at 40, which was the first time I questioned whether all this work and achievement I was doing was really working for me any more. I had benefited financially from the choices I'd made but I was a lost soul – I had nothing in my life that meant anything. I started asking a lot of questions at that point.

What is a good life? Is it more than achievements in the world and being busy doing things?

Cancer is a very harsh reminder that none of your achievements, your job title, your CV count for anything when all is said and done. What does my life mean then, when I look back and realise I gave it all to work? You don't need to have breast cancer to ask yourself these questions – I see it in my friendship circle too, as they go through mid-life and menopause. It's the search for a life where we can do some good and earn enough to have a nice life, but without living on stress.

Our generation was exceptionally lucky in that we got more freedom than any other generation of women, but we became trapped in something else – over-work and misidentification of what matters. I'm done with the struggle. Struggling to be successful in my career, struggling to keep up with the lifestyle. I don't need to find identity in work anymore; I have nothing to prove and nothing to achieve.

I'm very grateful for my life, but for all the benefits women of my generation have had, there is a fragility and a loneliness to our existence.

Women & ageing

When I was in my 40s, there was a different level of energy and physicality in my body. I was lifting heavy weights, taking HRT, I could still keep my weight down and wear skinny jeans. I wasn't as energetic as I had been at 25, but I didn't feel old.

I bought into the idea of being fit and sexy as you age. Age is just a number. 40 is the new 30, 50 is the new 40. I thought this was radical and challenging the status quo.

Now I've been ravaged by breast cancer and chemo and menopause, and I'm putting on weight, and my memory is so bad I don't know what day it is, and my sex drive has gone who knows where... I realise that this too was a story. Sure, it was a different story from the one that came before – the story that said we women were over the hill at 35 – but the new story was based on my value deriving from my looks, my physicality, and my youthfulness just as much as the one it replaced. I didn't realise how much I was trading on looking a certain way until I wasn't any of those things anymore.

It wasn't until I read back through my diary from the last year that I appreciated how much value I accrued from my looks and my body – my youthful appearance, the fact that I'm naturally slim and strong. And how much my internal self-esteem was based on it. I struggled with walking in the streets bald – because I was worried I wouldn't be considered attractive anymore. It's nuts right? To even be thinking about that when I'm in a life and death situation with cancer. And I've struggled with how I've looked over the last year since treatment ended. I feel that I've aged 10 years, my hair never looks right, I look tired. I miss looking in the mirror and seeing my former hot self looking back at me. But how odd to even be thinking about how I look rather than looking in the mirror and thinking "fuck yeah, you just survived cancer". It's a reminder of how deep the programming goes. It's not the measure of who I am, and I reject it, but it's there nonetheless.

I've had a lot of time this year to look around and to observe the images of ageing women we are shown. The media is suddenly full of a certain type of hot woman – 50+ but with beautiful hair and skin, 'perfect' slender bodies, and looking remarkably young. The post–50 woman is having a moment.

I'm 100% down with the idea that life doesn't have to be over at 50, and yes we should reject the old idea that we're on the scrapheap after a certain age, but is there ever a point where we can get off the treadmill of our looks and start to just be who we are?

To look slim and have barely a wrinkle at 50/60/70 means you either won the genetic lottery or you have a LOT of time and money and a great cosmetic surgeon. It feels like marketing to me – companies waking up to the idea that there's another demographic they can sell stuff to. We're simply perpetuating the ideas that have persecuted women for eons – that our value is in how we look, which of course means being thin and 'beautiful' in the way in which society has defined it – and continuing the fetishisation of youth.

Of course we can all admire youthful beauty. It's fun to check out someone who is hot. But this beauty is a moment in time. It's fleeting. Youth is for the young. We're meant to really enjoy it when it's ours, to live it fully, and then move on. Everything in nature has a season, and each season is beautiful in its own way. The human life is the same. We're meant to enjoy the seasons of our lives for what they are and then move on to the next.

And guess what? You can be sexy AF in every season – but for different reasons. Funny, smart, kind, wise – they can all be very sexy. You can be wrinkled and sexy, fat and sexy, old and sexy. Sexy does not just belong to those who are young-and-thin-in-appearance.

The autumn of our lives is about wisdom. Elders used to be the wisdom-keepers of the tribe. It's time to make wisdom cool, to make older women cool.

And what's so wrong with ageing anyway? There's a ton of money in Silicon Valley going into staving off the inevitable. Which is an intellectually fascinating problem for those rich guys who have the luxury of living to 150 and merging their consciousness with Artificial Intelligence, but the bigger problem is working out how we enable everyone else to be healthy within the current paradigm. Many of us die of so-called 'lifestyle' diseases – related to stress, diet, exercise and so on – and live our later years in pain, dealing with illness, consigned to old people's homes. Shouldn't we fix that first? Is there anything that bad about living a fixed lifespan, being happy and healthy for as much of it as possible, and then exiting gracefully?

I admire the older women who are fully expressed and fearless. Smart, funny, creative, wise. With faces that show they lived, that they had wild affairs, that they knew themselves and said what they thought and didn't care whether you approved of them. I'm drawn to the woman whose soul is etched into every line on her face, the ones who leave their own unique fingerprint on the universe – because it's what I want for myself. I want to be fully expressed – every last bit of me – before I die.

I spent way too many years caring about things that didn't merit it. I think the radical thing is to be free.

Surrender

My experience with breast cancer has been a masterclass in surrender. The concept of surrender is much talked about in personal development and spiritual circles. It's the idea that we wholeheartedly embrace a situation exactly as it is being delivered to us, and we let go of the idea that things should be anything other than as they are. It's trusting that everything is in divine right order, even when you can't see it or understand it yet.

All of this sounds easy; in fact it's exceptionally hard in the heat of real life, particularly when we're faced with life and death questions, and our own frailty and mortality.

In cancer there's a lot of surrender and letting go. We have to surrender to our diagnosis, to our treatment, to losing hair or parts of our body, to losing our life as we knew it, our identity. Sometimes we have to surrender life itself.

We have to surrender to not-knowing: We may never know what caused the cancer; We do treatments hoping they work but nothing is guaranteed; We sit in the not knowing afterwards – is the cancer coming back? We have to be able to deal with all of this and to find the courage to keep going, to remain cheerful and optimistic, and to hope for light at the end. It's a lot.

Why is surrender so hard?

Most of us live in a mind/ego/personality state, and the ego will not surrender. It cannot. And then along comes cancer, and we're faced with things beyond the ordinary – an illness and treatments that we don't understand and have limited control over, oceans of grief, and our own mortality. We're not equipped for any of this.

We cannot surrender without a fundamental trust in ourselves and in life. Without trust we're unable to plug in to our own innate resilience and feel confident that we can deal with whatever comes at us. We attempt to control events thinking that this will make us safe. On the cancer journey we have to wrestle with the life truth that there is no such thing as ultimate safety. At times we will all feel pain, suffer, feel defeated. And we will all die. The safety that we're looking for – guaranteed health and immortality – does not exist.

We don't surrender because we're terrified of facing reality – how hard this is, how we feel, how scared we are of treatment, loss, death. And because we change, and we resist that too.

We think we're more important than we are, and that our own suffering matters more than it does. Many of us are the product of western hyper-individualism: we want the universe to give us exactly what we think we want and become distressed when it doesn't. We have so many preferences for how we want things to be – and we only want good things, we don't want bad things. We don't see the big picture and we label things good or bad without realising that over the long term things that feel awful at the time can be the best thing that ever happened to you. And what is good or bad anyway?

How can we possibly surrender when we've been trained to want everything exactly the way we want it, and to feel entitled to this?

All of this is particularly hard for the alpha female – highly educated, brought up to believe in her own abilities, working in professional and highly competitive environments that require her to be ultra-strong in mind/personality/ego, and wrapped in armour. In this world our toughness is an advantage. But when faced with the existential nature of cancer it becomes our achilles heel. Because we cannot will this thing away. There's no amount of planning or money that can change what's happening, and the strength that works so well for you in other areas of your life becomes a barrier to surrendering deeply and being at peace with where you find yourself.

We fail to understand the true nature of things: that there are limitations to our power in this thing called life and that when all is said and done we are nothing but a blip – in a universe so grand we will never comprehend it, with infinity before us and infinity after us.

Surrender often happens by degree

Breast cancer has been a continuous process of surrender. I think I've surrendered, and then there's another level. There's always another level. And we can say the same about 2020/21 can't we? Just when we think we've processed a new reality there is more for us to let go of.

Are you really surrendered?

Many times on this path I thought I had surrendered, but really I was bargaining with the universe. "I surrendered to my hair loss, please don't take my eyebrows". "I've been so brave and strong through all of this, please don't take my powerlifting". None of this was me saying yes and being totally ok with whatever happens. None of it was me accepting it as if I chose it. But at the time I thought it was.

The positivity and strength we bring to our breast cancer journey – and our spiritual practices if we have them – can also be a barrier to surrender.

They can be a pretence of acceptance. We can be so busy in our positivity we avoid the real deal – sitting quietly with ourselves and tuning in to how we really feel about what's happening, and how this might be changing us.

Why does it matter?

Taking a stance of surrender/acceptance is less demanding energetically – fighting the impossible is exhausting and ultimately you cannot win in this situation. When you have an illness as serious as breast cancer you need all your energy for healing. There's a huge sense of peace when we give up fighting, an ease with things, and a grace under pressure..

When we put down our defences and soften into life all sorts of extraordinary things start happening. We become a different being, we start to understand the true nature of things. It changes everything.

The Nuances

It's important to be empowered on the cancer journey, in spite of how limited our choices are: asking questions, making our own decisions, having mastery of our emotional state as much as is possible. What we also need is the wisdom to know what we have the ability to control and what we don't, and the grace to accept the things we can't. This is how surrender and empowerment work together.

One of the problems with the word surrender is that it has connotations – of weakness, of giving in, of loss. Humans don't like loss, we just don't. I've realised it's easier to focus on what we're moving towards. It's not giving in, it's becoming someone who's able to play the game of life at a higher level.

Trusting yourself enough to be with life fully is terrifying but also thrilling. You're alive.

Cancer, life & death

In cancer you're face to face with your own mortality – probably for the first time. Many of us have never thought about our own death, or ever had a meaningful conversation about death and dying. Of course you can ignore this, but it's there anyway.

Breast cancer is a good cancer

"You've got cancer" is very quickly followed by "but it's a good one". What they mean is that 90% of us will still be alive in 5 years time. There are other cancers that are far "worse" to have. As soon as you have a cancer diagnosis you're into the world of talking and thinking about death, and having surreal conversations about your statistical chance of dying.

We live in a deeply death-phobic society

Death doesn't feature anywhere in our culture. We don't discuss how to die – how to face it, how to die a good death. Which is strange considering that every single one of us is going to have to do it. (Sidenote: this is one of the reasons that covid is having such an effect on humanity – death is suddenly in the collective consciousness and it's creating huge amounts of fear.)

The cultural assumption is that death is the worst thing that could happen and that our intention should be to avoid it at all costs. This means we force people to stay alive when the body can no longer function, rather than allowing a painless and graceful death. That scares me more than dying.

The cancer narrative is usually about how a person is fighting cancer, and if they died the narrative is how they lost their fight, which implies they somehow failed. Before I got cancer I never understood why people would refuse life-saving treatment. I get it now. The treatment is brutal – you submit to be cut up, poisoned, and radiated. You go half-way to death, and then stop at just the right point so that it will kill the cancer but not you. I can see why a person might reject the idea of fighting death at any price and instead choose to accept it's their time. It's very brave to know your own mind and make your own choices in the face of extreme pressure to keep going.

Talking about death is one of the last taboos

My experience has been that most people will go to any lengths to avoid a conversation about death. This is true even of people who have cancer, which surprised me the most. Whenever I've broached the subject of my own prognosis the response is mostly "you'll be fine"– as if other people might die but definitely not me. Which is clearly nonsensical. And then there's the "well we're all dying aren't we" response, which is insulting. And that's where the conversation stops. If you persist, people will push back to the point of arguing with you – this isn't something you should be talking about, you need to think positive! What they mean is: You're making me uncomfortable – can't you stop? I was repeatedly told I should see a therapist and treated as if there was something wrong with me. There was nothing wrong with me. There was only one person who asked me straight up "so how do you feel about death?" as if it was the most normal thing in the world. I was so grateful. After trying to initiate conversations about it many times I gave up and decided it was a thing to do on my own.

All the great mystics say that death is the greatest teacher

All the great mystics say that death is the greatest teacher and so I decided to see what they meant. I wanted to go all the way to the edge of life and see what was there. I encourage you to do this too: it turned out to be the most wonderful thing I've ever done for myself. It showed me how to fall in love with life.

I was completely blown away when I realised it wasn't fear of death that was bothering me – it was the fear that I hadn't lived. When I thought back over my life I had the awful feeling that I had wasted most of it. Of course there's a list of things I said I would do someday and that I never got around to: like many I've lived as if I was putting off happiness until some day in the future – a day that might never come now. But it was more than that. It was the feeling that I've been sleepwalking – living half a life and not daring to be me, or even to know myself, which felt unbelievably sad. It was the realisation that I've spent almost all my life working rather than living, because I had something to prove (to who?) which when all is said and done means I've traded my life and my freedom doing work I didn't believe in

to buy stuff that will all be junk when I'm dead. And have I done anything that matters? If I died tomorrow what would be the account of my life? How did I use my gifts and talents? It's hard to explain how it felt without using awful cliches – it was gut-wrenching.

When I got beyond all of that life-flashing-before-your-eyes stuff, however, what I found was the most extraordinary ecstasy at just being alive. When we dare to sit right on the line between life and death, we feel how tenuous our connection to life is, and something wonderful and beautiful happens. We're literally plugged into the supercurrent of the universe, and we experience a kind of divine awe and wonder and amazement. We feel alive with all of life. We know ourselves as love, the purest form of consciousness, and it's electric. And everything starts to make sense. There is the knowing that in the end nothing really matters, even our own lives. That we already have everything we need, that we are perfect just as we are. We realise that the prescription for life is to just fill your life with love and to not waste even a single day on anything else. And there is a desire to live – more than ever there is the desire to live, but to live differently. Once the divine has gotten "into the walls of your soul" (Caroline Myss) you cannot go back to normal, it's gone, there's no point even looking back, there's nothing there. This is what all the mystical poets write about: this knowing that there is so much more to this life than our day to day existence on the human plane.

How to sit with death

Meditation, contemplation, walking and thinking, doesn't matter how or where you do it. All we need to do is allow the idea that one day we will die to seep into our consciousness and watch our own reactions: the stories, the emotions, what we feel in our bodies. Be wholly with what comes up, don't reject any of it, and write it all down, draw, write poetry, cry, scream, walk, whatever you need. Allow yourself to feel what you feel. Trust that if you allow all the emotions – if you honour them – they will naturally subside, and that on the other side is the wisdom you're seeking.

And don't fear what feels like breaking, or heartbreak. You're not breaking: it's how we transition to another level of consciousness. It takes guts to allow your heart to be broken like this, and to have full trust in yourself. But you can do it – we all can. If you can't do this alone get a spiritual teacher or psychotherapist. Look for someone who isn't afraid to go all the way into the darkness with you – because they've been there before.

All there is is now

I got interested for a while in what I think happens after death. Is my soul eternal? Will I reincarnate? Or is it the end? The idea of reincarnation is comforting because it avoids confronting a hard ending. The idea that this is it and there is nothing more is hard for the human mind to bear. In the end, who knows anything for sure? It's the big mystery. Which brought me back to the idea that all there is is now. This life, today, here, now.

Death is capricious: she can just come and take you and there is nothing you can do about it. Realising this is an almighty shock

The grief

There's a big difference between real grief and just being upset about something. Death grief is like being disemboweled without anaesthetic. It's brutal – it's undiscriminating, it removes everything in its path. Which is exactly the point. It's also exquisite.

As I felt the grief subside I realised I didn't want it to end, which might sound odd. As overwhelming as it was, the grief was beautiful. I felt connected to something otherworldly and magical.

Love makes us feel this too. Which is why I started to riff on the idea that these two are the same, or they serve the same purpose – both of them animate the capacity of the heart, and we feel more, we love more.

I've experienced grief before – an end of relationship grief – that was so much it nearly took me under forever. I know how it feels to be lost in it and to wonder if there's a way out. We've all experienced this at one time or another, which is why grief is a thing that most of us tend to want to avoid.

But the grief at facing our own mortality is a different kind of grief. It's a deep existential grief. It's the grief that comes when we recognise that one day we will lose the only thing we really have – our 'one wild and precious life' (Mary Oliver). It's the grief that comes when we recognise that this is the only thing that matters and that we have spent a large chunk of it not fully appreciating this fact and wasting time. It's the grief that comes when we realise we have not fully lived, we have not allowed ourselves to fly and our time will one day run out. It's the grief at our absolute powerlessness – that for all our efforts, one day we will just be gone, and there is no begging, negotiating, or supplication to life that can change it.

Only those who have faced such massive truths will ever understand.

This grief was not sadness, although there were times I felt sad. Rather, the pain was soft and electrifying, almost erotic, most definitely a connection to the light, not a messenger from the darkness. And it didn't feel purposeless: my feeling was that it was doing something important to me. I had an image of the cosmos putting this gift of grief into my hands and knowing that I had just been given everything – a key to the secrets of the cosmos, a AAA pass to the meaning of life.

I've spent a lot of my life (nearly all of it) dealing with depression, or cynicism, a kind of "I could take it or leave it" attitude to things. This grief was showing me that that was a lie. That I wanted to live, very much, and that this half-arsed attitude wasn't good enough. The grief told me I was desperate – to really LIVE, to do everything I came here to do, and to do it now. It was time to stop pretending. It was calling out all my bullshit.

What I've noticed about grief is that it's almost a force of nature. It feels like it's bigger than you. It's not an emotion that can be controlled like so many others. It comes when it comes and you have to just stop what you're doing and allow it. I started calling the grief tears 'unspecific tears' – they didn't come as a response to my sitting at home thinking "I have cancer, and I might die soon". I

would be doing other things, getting on with life, and they would just come from nowhere. I wasn't depressed either, far from it, but the grief would still come.

And it works to its own timeframe – it lasts as long as it lasts. I noticed this was frustrating to those around me. I was expected to go back to normal or to be more positive – and I had no desire to do so. I was given a window into the secrets of the cosmos. What else could I possibly be doing that was more important or beautiful than this?

So grief, a thing we try to avoid, is actually the most sacred and holy of human experiences. It's destructive. It won't stand for any untruths, it's ruthless and brutal and clarifying. It strips you back to nothing – it's the toughest love there is.

But in this state of nothing the veils are thin, and we're able to touch the divine in a way we would find impossible any other way. We see beyond our smallness and come to know ourselves as cosmic beings.

There's no need to rush through it – it's essential to stay with it as long as you're able. And we must allow it to rip through – without defending any part of ourselves, without holding on to anything. This is the job the grief is here to do – to empty out all that needs to go, to make us ready for illumination. The more willing we are to go all the way in, the more we will let go of, the more we offer up to be washed clean, the greater the illumination. Our personal and spiritual growth in cancer is directly proportional to our ability to tolerate the discomfort and the misery of grief, without collapsing.

The dark night of the soul

I said to my soul, be still, and let the
dark come upon you
Which shall be the darkness of God
I said to my soul, be still, and wait
without hope
For hope would be hope for the wrong
thing; wait without love
For love would be love of the wrong
thing; there is yet faith
But the faith and the love and the hope
are all in the waiting.
Wait without thought, for you are not
ready for thought:
So the darkness shall be the light, and
the stillness the dancing.

T. S. Eliot, Four Quartets: "East Coker"

A dark night is when it feels as if all the light, all the meaning, has gone out of our lives. It's beyond feeling a bit sad or miserable, it's when we feel completely abandoned by life (or by God). The darkness feels like terror.

Although it feels that we've been abandoned, it is in fact the moment in the soul's journey where we're invited to awaken. It's an initiation, a time of complete transformation. You go in as one person and come out as another. Speak to anyone who's had one and they'll likely say the terror felt real, but if they could go back in time they would still do it. Nothing is ever the same afterwards.

The difference between a dark night and depression

In my experience (I've had it most of my life) depression is when we get stuck in our pain and our stories, going over and over the same ground, unable to move forward. A dark night will sometimes feel like depression, but the difference comes from curating the experience for what it is – a transformation. It's not futile at all. It's a deliberate and conscious allowing of our own destruction in order to experience the next level of consciousness.

There will be several times in a person's life when they're invited or forced into darkness. It doesn't have to be a brush with cancer, it could be a relationship breakdown, a death, the mid-life crisis, an existential crisis.

When we know what they are (I've done 3 and counting) we can say to ourselves "hello dark night, my friend, here we are again". We know the process, we have faith that it's the pathway to illumination. It's a moment of great maturity – to say yes when a dark night comes knocking, and to take yourself all the way into the darkness and back, alone.

The highs and the lows

A dark night is exhilarating and terrifying in equal measure. It's as alone as you will ever feel, and as alive as you will ever be. It's a journey to hell and back. You will be stripped of everything, and when you think you're as bare naked as it's possible to be, you will be asked for more. For as long as you're holding on to anything that is not truth, you will be trapped in this hell with no way out. You must become nothing. No-thing. It will feel like coming completely undone, an existential free-fall. You're in darkness, and you're alone and you will feel that you're wandering around and around, completely and utterly lost.

All your fears will appear as if from nowhere to terrorise you: you will feel that you're drowning under the weight of the sadness and regret and anger. There will be times when you feel that you're on fire from the inside – and you are, in a spiritual sense. Fire is the energy of transformation. You will fall out of love with large parts of your life, and feel completely disenchanted with the world. Things that used to mean so much seem pointless, and you will feel lost without the old anchors. There will be a realisation that you don't know who you are, or that you're not who you thought you were, or that you don't like who you think you are, or that this version of you has run its course. You will have moments when you look out and see everyone else (apparently) sailing through life and feel anger, envy, and bitterness that this is your lot. Why is this happening to me? You might find yourself sitting waiting to be rescued. You might become frustrated or angry that no-one has swooped in to save you. You cannot move on until you realise it's on you. All of your life – it's on you.

At times it feels like too much to bear and you will beg for it to stop. You bargain with life to take you back to safe ground – to who and where you were before this all started.

You will be frustrated that your go-to tactics and techniques for making yourself feel better stop working, in fact they will often make you feel 'worse'. This is because these are practices that we use to change how we feel about what's happening, rather than practices designed to take us deeper into the reality of where we find ourselves, and to learn to withstand this.

You will realise that the self-help books don't work, and that there is no guru/healer who can help you, and that you're really all alone. That this is your process, no-one else can help you, and that it can only be this way. Being alone is a fundamental and necessary part of this process: you're learning to stand alone in the middle of the darkness without fear. You will ache for the light. You will wonder what is wrong with you that others have it and not you. Did I do something so terrible that I don't deserve it? You will fear that you will never make it, that you will never escape this darkness. Your longing becomes a kind of madness. There is nothing that you wouldn't trade to touch the light, even for just for a minute.

On the other hand there is ecstasy. You touch the divine, and it changes you forever. The words of the English language are insufficient to describe the true nature of this thing: You will be consumed by a desire to know love unbounded, to be it, to be reborn of it. There is an exquisite sense that you're engaged in a beautiful and sacred process, of bringing yourself back to life. There is a feeling of being more alive than you have ever felt, which is as all-consuming and erotic as the feeling of meeting a new lover and falling in love. And you are, but it's a different kind of love, it's a love for all of humanity, and the earth, and a love for yourself you never knew was possible. It's a super-charged kind of love, love as a force that powers the universe. It feels magical.

The Surrender

Eventually you will reach a point where you realise that safety doesn't exist, and it never did – you were living the illusion of safety – there is nothing to go back to. That the only way through is to keep moving deeper into this thing – deeper inside of yourself. There's no way back, no half-measures, this is it And that all you have is You. No-one and nothing can help you here and that's the point.

You stop trying to do stuff to fix the problem – none of it is working. You stop resisting the process. You allow the destruction. You understand that you have to completely break, to let go of absolutely everything that you thought and believed in. You give up your fear of breaking and you beg for it. You will likely be on your knees at this point – and there is no shame in that, it's where you need to be.

Instead of action, you learn to just sit and be here now, without trying to be 'spiritual' or do anything at all. You experience it all, and you wait, and you trust. You learn grace – the ability to bear this, to expand to such a size that you can hold all of this pain and more, the humility to break and let go, the respect for yourself and your courage

to be here and doing this. You get still and quiet and deep. For women used to getting their way by action, determination, and force, this will feel agonising. It's hard to countenance the idea of doing nothing, it goes against everything we've been taught. But trust me: this is the way.

Once you surrender, things eventually start to shift of their own accord, and everything you wanted all this time begins to show up. Something lifts, you feel lighter, you wake up with a new sense of how great it is to be alive, you see beauty all around you. Your connection to the divine becomes the only thing that matters.

You start to hear the voice you've been longing to hear – this is You. You are Home. And You are Divine.

A glorious human spirit, who has the great fortune to be having this incredible cosmic adventure called Life.

Spirituality

"A hundred years of education is nothing compared to one moment spent with God."

~ Shams of Tabriz, Rumi's Guru

I've had a devoted spiritual practice for years; I was sure of a lot of things. These days I would call myself more of a mystic – devoted to the mystery, and comfortable knowing nothing.

It turns out breast cancer is really hard. In a brutal fashion, she removes everything from your life – says to you no you're not your hair, no you're not your job or your money or your stuff, no you're not your stories or your personality, your likes and dislikes, no you're not your plans or your achievements.

We are stripped of all our artifices and pretences and crutches, our attachments to the components that make up a human life.

It happens by degree, one bit at a time, until you're beaten into submission. You think you've given everything and then you're asked for more, and more, until you feel that you've become nothing. It's the feeling of having walked through the eye of a needle. You have to let go of everything though, or it's no deal. What I didn't understand at the time is that in the act of becoming nothing I would end up knowing myself as the cosmos itself – it was extraordinary. One of those moments when the consciousness is stretched so much it can never return to normal. I resisted this becoming nothing, not realising that it was the very point of the thing. That this is your one moment spent with God, your 'reward' for staying the course.

I am more convinced than ever that for many of us suffering is what we need to move from one level of consciousness to another.

Would I say I'm glad I had breast cancer? No-one would say they want cancer. But has it been a fast-track to things I couldn't have experienced any other way? I could have meditated for 100 years and not even come close to what I know now.

I thought my spirituality was going to 'save' me from the worst of the thing, that I would sail through it. That feels very naive to me now.

I started off strong, but pretty soon I had to abandon all of it – I had to stop trying to be spiritual, to be anything actually, and to just trust my instinct.

It turns out we know what to do when we dare to trust ourselves, and it's often only when our back is against the wall that we're willing to do it. I learned to trust myself – I claimed myself – which is a very big deal.

In many ways my spirituality was a hindrance. Along the way I had absorbed a bunch of new age ideas, that may or may not be true, but they're not at all helpful when you have cancer. The idea that I should be able to heal myself with love, for instance, which became a huge obstacle when I had to put myself through chemo – it felt like failure and made the whole thing harder.

I struggled because I was having so many emotions – if I was evolved spiritually shouldn't I be able to rise above these things? Would the Buddha have been able to do cancer and not have emotions? After trying to transcend my fear and again feeling like a failure, I decided the point was to be with my experience exactly as it was – the fear, the misery, the pain, the shock and grief of death. Being able to face these things and not collapse is your victory in this thing.

Rather than avoiding emotions we can view them as the firewalk on the way to illumination. We can honour our suffering and attend to it, and in this way it heals – we weave it into the story of our lives. There's great beauty in our epic struggle.

I probably used to believe in the 'love and light' thing. This phraseology started to drive me nuts as I went deeper into cancer. It's easy to say love and light when things are going the way you want them to, and a lot harder when you're sucking on a bag of lemons. It felt like such a cliche. No matter how spiritual you are, the reality of cancer is brutal. Sometimes you gotta take gruesome medicine to survive, and sometimes you're going to be crying on the bathroom floor.

What cancer takes in fact is a lot of courage, strength of spirit, and a massive dose of humility – to keep going when you feel diabolical, and when the light feels so far away you're not sure it even exists.

I've felt lonely for most of my life. Not human lonely, I have friends. Existentially alone. The illusion of separateness would be the spiritual diagnosis of the problem. Before this I'd had a teacher, an intermediary. Now there was just me, in all my suffering, reaching out to the light and asking for help. Although on a human level I was very alone, I never felt abandoned. The grace I felt on this journey was something else. It's not logical, it's otherworldly, and I can't explain it, but there was something achingly beautiful about it.

My previous spiritual 'aspiration' (yes that's ironic) was reaching for the stars. I thought there was somewhere else, a place better than this, and that if I meditated hard enough I would make it there. Having faced death I'm no longer looking to escape. I am here.

There is now. And that is it. There may or may not be somewhere else after this. But for now I'm here doing this.

After a lifetime of thinking about it I finally worked out the meaning of life – it is simply to be here and to be fully alive.

Before this I didn't dare to admit what my heart craved. But then things got tough and my reaction was to turn to the divine. It was the only thing that made sense in the face of something I had no idea how to handle. It was when I finally said it's you and me God. Show me it all, I'm here for it.

So many of us crave to know who and what we really are, to know the secrets of the universe – and yet we're terrified to go in search of it. We prefer to live in not knowing the full magical extent of things, out of fear. Instead we choose to live a fraction of a life. No more. I'm here for all of it.

"Dear companions,
We have been in love
with God
For so very, very long."

~ Hafiz

Loving yourself through it

A lot of us have a really complicated relationship with our bodies. I grew up hating mine.

I can't do that now. It doesn't make sense. My body's having to endure so much, all I can do is love her. It feels right. I sense, too, that she knows exactly what to do to recover and that I don't need to do much except to eat and sleep.

I look at myself in the mirror these days and I see a very different person looking back at me than I did when this all started. It's all played out on my body in some way.

After my surgeries, I had 2 huge red scars, and uneven strange-looking breasts since they took a lump out of one, and my bruising hadn't gone months later. There was pain and swelling whenever I pushed myself too hard.

There was the chemo - of course I lost my hair, but did you know you lose every other hair on your body too? No pubes or eye lashes either? It's weird. And your nails peel off. After chemo, when there was so much nausea I couldn't eat for days at a time, I would lose kilos in weight, and I looked emaciated and fragile. So fragile. And there's the dry and scaley skin, and looking sort of grey - pallid. Deathly

I suppose you could call it. Even my eyeballs would hurt.

I've also been forced into menopause and I already feel the absence of the hormones – my skin is saggy and I'm definitely ageing. Although that's probably the treatment too. I get weird pains in my body. I'm losing the muscle I used to love so much from years of training and I don't know if my strength is ever coming back.

But I've never for one second allowed any loathing of my body in. Look what she's coming back from! How could I not think she totally freaking rocks?

Throughout all of this I look in the mirror and talk directly to her - I love you, you've got this, I know you know what to do. I consciously send love to every cell in my body.

We must love ourselves too. More so on the hardest days - when you can't seem to find the strength or the positivity to keep going, when you make mistakes, when you're cranky or emotional. No good can come from any other way. We must be utterly devoted to ourselves, our healing, our courage in the struggle of this thing, our victories, big or small. This in itself is healing. When we face ourselves and say I love you, you're doing great, we finally meet ourselves. It's a powerful and beautiful moment.

THE HEROIN

E'S JOURNEY

What is a rite of passage?

A rite of passage is a formal way of marking and enabling a significant transition in a person's life: puberty, marriage, childbirth, menopause, the mid-life years, illness, death. These are not the kinds of life changes that we just breeze through: in a rite of passage our sense of identity fundamentally and permanently changes, as do many aspects of our lives.

Rites fascinate me so much because we humans need them – ceremony and ritual enable us to welcome transformation no matter how gruelling it may be. And yet our modern world almost entirely ignores them – they're seen as features of less civilised societies.

In traditional rites of passage there will be initiations – cutting off the hair, going solo into the wild, fasting, life and death physical challenges – all of which are designed specifically to remove the initiate from their old identity and propel them forward. All sounds like cancer, right?

We opt in to some of these rites – marriage for instance – and others are forced upon us. Those that are forced upon us are often harder to navigate: we didn't ask for the change, we don't want it, and this makes the whole thing more traumatic.

That said, we do always have a choice about how we navigate them when they arrive: we can choose to resist the transformation on offer and maintain the status quo – or we can say yes. Resistance will often make the process harder than it needs to be.

In truth we're always in transition – in every life there are times that we must leave an old self behind, and become someone and something new. In fact life is a never-ending process of becoming, and everything that happens to us is a prompt to become more of who and what we really are.

Cancer is such a powerful rite, in part because the treatment itself is so arduous – we respond by digging deep, we have no choice. But it's also because the recognition of our own mortality triggers a journey in search of the true meaning of life.

We are rewarded greatly however: we meet our true selves, we find powers we didn't know we had, and we get a hotline to the divine.

I coined the phrase *The Heroine's Journey* to describe this process because cancer is a trial of such epic proportions. You're going to be tested.

The power of a rite of passage

Viewing this experience as a rite of passage provides you with meaning and inspiration for what lies ahead. The human brain needs a story, we survive on meaning.

Rites of passage tend to follow a structure. Those who came before you have given you the tools to navigate the terrain, which enables you to deal with each part of the journey and it's different challenges.

There's a sense of agency that comes from consciously moving through the steps and curating our own experience. In the face of so much that's wholly out of our control we are still the owner of our experience, even if we don't 'like' parts of what life is serving up. I am at the centre of this story, not the cancer, not the treatments, not the grief.

It's an anchor in the dark moments to know that your cancer is not just an existential freefall with no purpose. You trust that something 'good' will come from this, even when you feel so lost in the darkness of the illness you have no idea where you are or what you're doing. We can say yes to allowing this journey to do what it's going to do to us.

There's a very special energy that's created when you designate an experience as a rite of passage: it's

mystical, it's sacred, it's holy – it's powerful. It offers massively accelerated personal and spiritual growth.

We can make the process beautiful in spite of things. Whether by rituals, ceremonies, writing, creating, whatever is your jam. The human mind responds to beauty. It makes life better, it elevates us above the mundane and the misery.

One of the features of cancer is that it's very very lonely. There's a profound spiritual comfort in knowing you're not the first and you won't be the last woman to make this journey, and you're united with these others in an invisible but quite beautiful way.

Be the heroine of your own Journey ♡

The phases

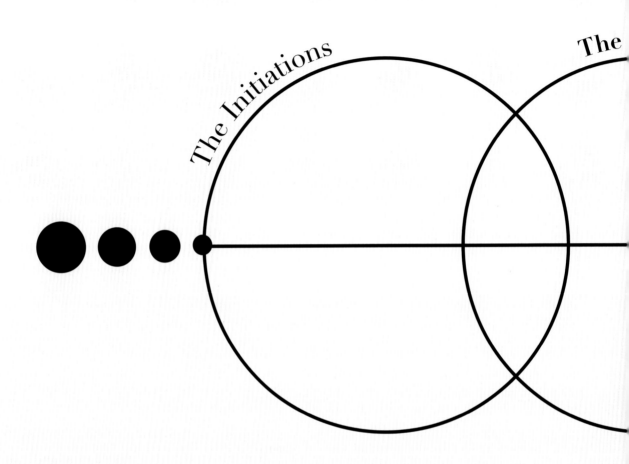

The Initiations

The

The Initiations

A cancer diagnosis is a shock. The moment it happens you're no longer the person you were and there is no going back. It's an ending, and also the beginning of your rite of passage. In a heartbeat we enter another dimension, there is a before and an after. Then we go into treatment, with each one removing another layer of our lives and our identities and taking us further and further away from our old selves and the people around us.

The Liminality

We are in-between worlds. Our old life and identity is gone, and we don't yet know what's next. We're so far into the cancer journey we can no longer see the shore; we don't know yet what any of this means or what the future holds.

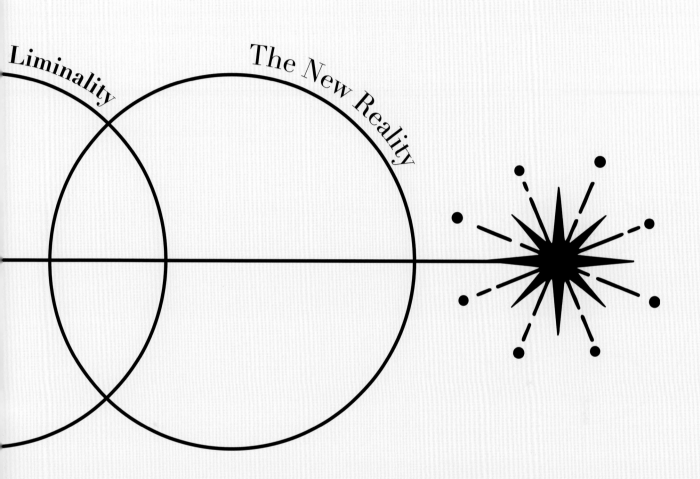

Liminality

The New Reality

The New Reality

What is the new reality? How can we accept it? How do we find peace, whatever our future looks like?

Features of the phases

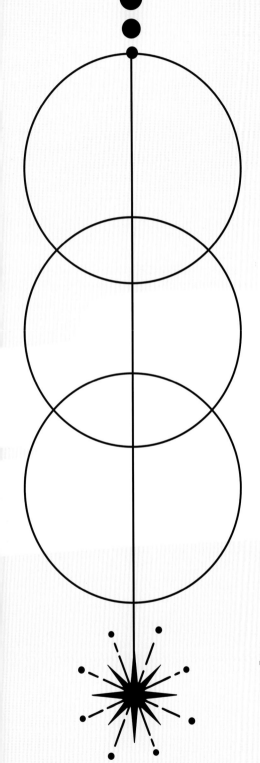

The Initiations

The Liminality

The New Reality

Cognitive dissonance/denial:
Wait, what, I have cancer? I don't
understand. Are you sure this
isn't a mistake? You find yourself
suddenly living a life that's not
yours. Who am I now?

The emotional storm: This kicks
in immediately – every emotion
under the sun, particularly fear.

Grief: We start to process the
shock of what's happened, we
face our own mortality, and the
grief hits.

The new reality: Who am I
now? What sense do I make
of this? How do I be at peace
with what's happened? What
happens now? What does my
life mean?

Separation: Right away there is a distance between us and others – we are now a person with cancer. In spite of the support we may have, in many ways we're on our own.

Spiritual resolve: The feeling of being superhumanly strong. I say yes. I'm open to knowing what needs to heal, andwhat this thing can teach me.

Overwhelm & Exhaustion: We're firefighting, there's not much time to think or process. We have to ingest lots of information, make decisions and get on with things even though this is as tired as you've ever been, and we feel fragile and vulnerable. .

Loss: We have to let go of parts of our bodies, our hair, our health, our identity, friends, our lives as we knew them. We are ground down to a husk of ourselves. We start to understand that parts of ourselves and our lives are ending, that some things will never be the same.

The crash: Feeling flat, depressed, angry, confused, tired, a sense of existential futility. We can lose our faith in life.

The nothingness: After big-time grief you will likely feel that you've been emptied out on every level. It can feel like 'not knowing' which can be extremely disorienting, but it can also bring a sense of space and peace – a blessed relief after the drama and emotion of what has preceded it.

Healing: It's a time to ask what needs to heal: Repairing the body; Doing the inner work; Making peace with what has happened. Spiritually, this is when we start to seek the wisdom.

Awe and joy: We start to get a sense of having traversed a most difficult journey. We sense how precious life is and how magical the cosmos is. There is clarity on what matters.

What will help you on your journey

Self devotion
Being able to hold ourselves with love and tenderness, knowing what you need and being able to give it to yourself, being entirely devoted to your healing and self-care.

Love
Able to offer and receive love, loving the fabric of our day to day life, a love of life itself.

Surrender
An ability to say yes to what's happening, to be with things as they are, to receive help, to keep our heart open and stay soft under pressure.

Wisdom
Knowing when to fight and when to surrender, trusting yourself and your knowing/intuition, knowing what needs to heal, able to make the right decisions in your best interests, able to find the gold in the midst of it all.

Grace
Being able to connect to the presence of divinity that is in you and all around you and to find refuge there, able to rise above and to be thankful for life regardless.

Courage
The ability to dig deep when you're tired and scared, to find a way to just keep going, to not collapse in the face of things.

Sovereignty
Emotional mastery, being in command of ourselves regardless of circumstance, empowered to make decisions and to own our experience.

Navigating the underworld
Able to sit with loss, grief, death, the not knowing of this journey, and to take ourselves though a dark night.

Metamorphosis
Saying yes to this rite of passage, the ability to recognise what is changing, ending or leaving our lives and to be at peace with it, the power to transform ourselves.

THE HEROINE'S JOURNEY

[BRE]AST CANCER

RES + RECOVER

[KADIO]
- EXPULSION
  I POST ONLY

THE GRIEF
- GRIEF
- LOCKDOWN/ LIFE
- PIL
- HINTS OF UPWARDS TREND

THE LIMINALITY
- SPIRITUALITY
- TRANSFORMATION
- NOT KNOWING WHAT NEXT
  NOT
  ~~FINISHED/RESOLVED~~

[...] GETS
[...] DARK
[...]ALITY
[...]S

Grace Transforms everything you experience

Real doesn't know completely disturbing
- you can recognise it still keep going

Whale did it all go wrong?
Not 'Wrong' just when did I choose to not live?

I am the solely am looking for

I am the safety I'm looking for

I will never have a foot in another world

The gift of tears

What in me needs to heal?

Real/white chapel page style

BREAST GLOBAL	CANCER DATA

o o o o o

PREVIEW

Be the heroine of your own Journey

Be the heroine of your own Journey

THE WORLD

THE LIMINALITY

GRIEF
A DARK NIGHT
[HEALING]
ILLUMINATION
NO TURNING BACK

THE NEW REALITY

Preamble how to move forwards

ACCEPTANCE
MEANING / IDENTITY
FACING FORWARDS

Be the heroine of your own Journey

Acknowledgements

My eternal thanks to all the people who helped me
during these last 2 years, in ways big or small. I love you.

My gratitude to the wonderful people who helped me
bring this project to life:

Pre-op tests and operation day photos by Rochelle Tissa
rochelletissa.com
Instagram @rochelletissa

Book and web design by Harri Sheffer
studiohu.co
Instagram @studiohudesign

Book publishing support by Michael Hanrahan
Publish Central
publishcentral.com.au/
facebook.com/PublishCentral

Statistics and other support by Lisa Renkin
linkedin.com/in/lisa-renkin-410ba311/

Moral support by Henry Roth
facebook.com/henryandfriendslive

Stay in touch

Put yourself on the mailing list
tntabc.com

Follow me
instagram.com/iamjanemarshall
#TNTABC

Email me direct
janemarshallis@gmail.com

It is love alone that gives worth to all things.

~ Teresa of Ávila

Disclaimer
The material in this publication is of the nature of general comment only, and does not represent professional advice. It is not intended to provide specific guidance for particular circumstances and it should not be relied on as the basis for any decision to take action or not take action on any matter which it covers. Readers should obtain professional advice where appropriate, before making any such decision. To the maximum extent permitted by law, the author and publisher disclaim all responsibility and liability to any person, arising directly or indirectly from any person taking or not taking action based on the information in this publication.